THE JOAN COLLINS' FAN CLUB

MY LIFE
WITH
FANNY
THE
WONDER
DOG

*THE
TRUE
STORY*

JULIAN CLARY
AND
PAUL MERTON

M
PAPERMAC

First published 1989 by
PAPERMAC
a division of Macmillan Publishers Limited
4 Little Essex Street London WC2R 3LF
and Basingstoke

Associated companies in Auckland, Delhi, Dublin, Gaborone, Hamburg,
Harare, Hong Kong, Johannesburg, Kuala Lumpur, Lagos, Manzini,
Melbourne, Mexico City, Nairobi, New York, Singapore and Tokyo

ISBN 0-333-49926-3

A CIP catalogue record for this book is available from the British Library

Photography: Peter Mountain
Design: Abrahams Pants

Typeset by Bookworm Typesetting, Manchester
Printed in Hong Kong

*Dedicated to
anyone who
has ever lived
in a bed-sit*

Dear reader, let me take you on a journey backwards in time. The year is 1924, the place London. A handsome young man is mincing down Mare Street towards the Hackney Empire. It is raining but he doesn't care. Tonight he is meeting his girl. The young man's name is Albert Fan Club and he is in love. Talullah Stanwyke is the most beautiful girl in Hackney (which isn't saying much) and she has a feeling in her water that tonight Albert is going to propose. Half an hour later she is flat on her back behind the fish shop. She has a ring on her finger, a smile on her face and a fish cake where the sun don't shine. She handles him roughly, demanding every ounce of his masculinity.

'Oh Albert,' she breathes.
'Do you really love me?'

'I wouldn't be lying on these wet cobblestones if I didn't,' he whispers in reply.

And, as she gazes up at him, the yellow glow from a distant gas light reveals more than just a man . . . there are six people watching. And one of them is selling programmes.

So, dear reader, this display of affection was the first public performance ever given by a member of the Fan Club family.

But it wasn't to be the last.

CHAPTER ONE

PRE-FANNY DAYS

'SATIRE IS A SORT OF GLASS WHEREIN BEHOLDERS DO GENERALLY DISCOVER EVERYBODY'S FACE BUT THEIR OWN.' JONATHAN SWIFT.

My childhood was spent in Teddington, a leafy suburb of London. I was an imaginative child; I used to frolic with the pixies in the wood until the police caught me at it. On rainy days I would play with my farmyard set. Miniature cows, pigs and sheep would be set out on my green bedroom carpet. The owner of the farm was Tom, who would sit astride his blue tractor, surveying his land as far as the wardrobe. Although his legs were bent permanently into the sitting position, he always had a good word for the ducks. His wife Jill was much smaller than him because she was made to an entirely different scale. Although the chickens towered above her she showed no fear and went about her duties with a smile and a bucket.

One Christmas I was presented with a plastic hippopotamus and it quickly became a feature of the farm. I often imagined the conversation between Tom and Jill when they got up to milk the cows on Boxing Day morning and found a hippo in the yard.

Jill: *What the bleedin' 'ell's that, Tom?**

Tom: *It's one of God's creatures and we must give it a home.*

Jill: *Well I ain't mucking it out.*

Tragedy was to hit the farm several years later when Monty,
the neighbour's dog, made a meal of Jill's lower limbs. She still
got about but spent most of her days thereafter leaning against the fence.

Footloose and fancy-free, I was to spend many happy hours
playing with that farmyard, where the animals lived long and
happy lives and market day never arrived.

As I grew into a tall and beautiful adolescent I realised that
I wanted more than Tom and his farmyard.* I escaped into books.
In fact I once spent ten days in the middle of *Wuthering Heights*.
Heathcliff taught me how to build a camp fire and Cathy showed me
how to do things with a crochet hook that I had never thought
possible.**

By my late teens I'd managed to define what I was yearning for: something living but not necessarily human. I went out with Kevin.

It lasted three minutes.

The next few years were a fruitless meander through the sordid avenues of human experience. I was a wreck, a ruin and a shrine to despair, until finally, dear reader, I reached rock bottom . . . I became a STUDENT. Like the thousands of sad-eyed individuals around me, I paced the corridors in search of knowledge and companionship. I wore the mask of a happy-go-lucky drama student, prancing about in many an amateur production, but at night I cried myself to sleep.

Surely there must be more to life? And before long there would be.

CHAPTER TWO

PUPPY LOVE

'"LET'S FIGHT TILL SIX AND THEN HAVE DINNER," SAID TWEEDLEDUM.' LEWIS CARROLL.

My college days over, I joined the ranks of the un–
employed (soon I became a lance-corporal*).

Every other Tuesday at half past ten I would
shuffle along the queue to Box C. In an attempt
to break the monotony of this depressing ritual,
I would sometimes play games with the tight-
lipped staff of the DHSS. These first clumsy
attempts at comedy were never successful.
'Hello tight lips' didn't raise a smile, so I
quickly made the move into visual gags.
One November morning I signed on
dressed as Ethel Merman – still nothing.
I grew obsessed with the man behind the
window at Box C. His surly countenance
would haunt my very dreams. My Ethel
Merman had failed, but perhaps where
she had been found wanting Bilko
would succeed. A fortnight's
preparation went down the drain
when I forgot my lines.** I walked
home with my bald wig and glasses,
weeping with despair.

Over the next few months I was
to try a veritable pot-pourri of
characters both real and fictional.
I developed themes: March to June
1981 saw my tribute to the Hollywood musical – they still
talk about my Debbie Reynolds. Then I went mad. For
several months I became Sid James. Friends stopped
visiting and my life was in turmoil.

And still the man at Box C didn't crack a smile.

*I LIKED THE UNIFORM.

**SO WHAT'S NEW?

And then one day, arriving late at the dole office, I snagged my Tricel cardi on the wheels of an abandoned pram and hurtled to the front of the queue, cracking my head against the glass partition of window C. As I slumped to the ground, battling against unconsciousness, I finally heard the laugh I had so desperately tried to evoke. I saw his grotesque cackling face above me and I felt no pain. Only joy. Pure unsurpassed JOY.

From then on my life changed. I became a different person. I travelled more, even to the extent of going south of the river. I just didn't care. One late September afternoon, I found myself in the vicinity of Battersea Dogs Home. At the distant yapping of a thousand homeless dogs I felt strangely drawn. My heart pounded with a passion I couldn't begin to comprehend. I sensed a madness overwhelming my very core; a madness that in a simultaneous moment of golden joy both confused and yet beckoned me towards a new world of understanding and canine magic.

Suddenly I stopped and sniffed the air . . .

'A mongrel,' I murmured. 'I must buy a mongrel!'

I opened the magnificent gates, wide-eyed
with excitement. As dogs homes go this one had
gone – damp patches, bits dropping off, and
that was just the woman who ran the place.

Kennel after kennel I passed, gazing desperately
at the inhabitants for that kindred spirit that I
now knew had four legs and a tail. Suddenly I
froze. In a cage before me a beautiful honey-

coloured mongrel, with the air of Garbo and the
legs of a whippet, eyed me wistfully through the
rusty iron bars. It was Fanny. Above us two
doves pirouetted in the sky. They danced as only
lovers can.*

I stood enchanted. She was the
most beautiful creature I had
ever seen. Who knows how
long we stood like that, gazing
into each other's eyes.

The mood was broken when the
kennel maid came up behind me
with a broom handle.

*IN THE NUDE.

CHAPTER THREE

THE EARLY DAYS

'WHO CAN FORETELL FOR WHAT HIGH CAUSE THIS DARLING OF THE CROSS WAS BORN?' ANDREW MARVELL.

Later that day I smuggled Fanny into my lodgings. Perhaps 'lodgings' is too fancy a word for the cramped attic room I called home. I paid fifteen pounds per week for the privilege of living there. Mr Bishop, the landlord, would knock at my door every Wednesday, reeking of creosote and seeking sexual satisfaction.

He was lucky to get the rent. Pinned to the fridge door was a list of rules and regulations.

Rule 1: No fridges allowed

Rule 2: No yodelling

Rule 3: Nobody allowed in rooms after dark. Tenants included.

Rule 4: NO DOGS

This presented me with a thorny problem – how was I to conceal young Fanny from the beady eye of Mr Bishop? At first I contrived to meet him on the stairs, rent book at the ready, but soon he became suspicious.

'Mr Fan Club,' he breathed. *'I would like to inspect your room.'*

And with that he brushed past me, not missing the opportunity to tweek and fondle as he went.* Sensing my nervousness he kicked open the door, pointed at Fanny and said, *'What's that, Mr Fan Club?'*

'It's an ornamental cactus from Camden Market,' I blurted out, still tender from his tweeking.

'Cactus?' he hissed, not yet convinced of my story.

'Let me show you,' I said, placing the now growling Fanny into a flower pot and giving her a liberal sprinkling of Baby Bio.

'Oh yes,' he said, clearly relieved. *'I will see you next Wednesday then.'*

And with that he left, pausing only to ejaculate over the bed-spread.

As the sound of his footsteps disappeared, Fanny leapt on to my lap. Somehow she knew we were going for a walk ... to Sketchley.

It may surprise the reader to learn, as it indeed surprised me, that Fanny was not confused by these elaborate subterfuges. She played her roles magnificently, disguising herself on various occasions as a dustpan and brush, a television set and, in one moment of sheer inspiration, Hartlepool.

*HE WAS A TWEEKER AND A FONDLER IF EVER THERE WAS ONE. I WOULD ESTIMATE 40% TWEEK AND 60% FONDLE. BUT I HAD A FEELING THAT HE COULD TAKE OR LEAVE HIS TWEEK. FOR HIM THE TWEEK WAS A MERE PRELUDE TO THE SERIOUS BUSINESS OF FONDLING. I OFTEN FELT THAT HIS HEART WASN'T IN THE TWEEK, HE COULDN'T GET IT OVER QUICK ENOUGH. WHEREAS ME, I'M THE OTHER WAY ROUND.† I COULD TWEEK ALL NIGHT AND I WOULDN'T CARE IF I NEVER FONDLED AGAIN.

†WE ALL KNOW THAT.

These were early indications that perhaps Fanny was more than just an ordinary dog. I also noticed that unlike other dogs who would greet their owners with, say, a newspaper and a pair of slippers when they returned home, Fanny would be busy putting the finishing touches to a ratatouille. And imagine my surprise when one summer's evening I opened the door and found her tossing a salad.*

Her behaviour with other dogs, however, was still basic. A walk in the park swiftly degenerated into a bum-sniffing contest. She had no time for small dogs, giving them but a cursory glance as she scanned the horizon for bigger and better fry. The silhouette of a well-hung labrador was enough to send her scurrying across the park, with me, ever the watchful parent, not far behind. On one occasion I got into a nasty fight with a bad-tempered alsatian. When this vicious brute bared its teeth at my Fanny I saw red. I faced the devilish mutt head-on, but as I stared into its wild blood-shot eyes it dawned on me that flapping the lead and shouting *'Shoo!'* wasn't going to be enough. There was only one course of action open to me: sarcasm. I stung him to the quick with a series of acid comments, focusing in turn on the shape of his ears, the texture of his fur and finishing off with an unnecessary reference to half-eaten babies in prams. After a minute or two of this he skulked off, his tail between his legs, ashamed to be an alsatian.**

*A HABIT SHE PICKED UP FROM MR BISHOP NO DOUBT.

**YEARS LATER I WAS TO USE A SIMILAR TECHNIQUE UPON UNRULY MEMBERS OF MY AUDIENCE. BUT MORE OF THAT LATER.

At about this time I had secured a position with the 'Get 'Em Off' Singing Telegram Agency. My duties were many and varied. My brief was to appear at office parties, wedding receptions, birthday gatherings or whatever, dressed as a character of the client's choosing. Be it Don Juan, Cupid, or, as on one memorable occasion, Gordon Honeycombe. The driving force behind 'Get 'Em Off' was Kiki Dunbarton, a former Tiller Girl whose looks had faded about the time of the Macmillan Government but who managed to satisfy her appetite for rough gin and dope by persuading young people like myself to prance about in scanty costumes for a measly pittance.

I liked her.

She would sit on her swivel chair in a Ra-Ra skirt, a bow in her hair, a joint in one hand, swigging gin out of a hot water bottle.

'Hello my love,' she would say. 'Got a job for you.' There was no guessing what these jobs might be, but most popular was the Tarzan- gram. And this was to prove my undoing. Having no car I travelled by public transport, and one Saturday night I arrived, according to my instructions, at the crowded Kings Head pub on the Edgware road. I threaded my way through the packed saloon bar and located my victim, one Debbie Snout. She was obviously an audio typist, in the throes of celebrating her eighteenth birthday with Malibu and friends. Keeping my identity secret I made my way to the gentlemen's latrine. Once inside the cubicle I quickly changed into my alter ego –

Tarzan

Lord of the Jungle

Pausing only to hide my clothes above
the cistern and tuck a banana into my
loin-cloth, I burst back into the heavily
populated watering hole. Five minutes and
fifteen pounds of humiliation later I returned
to the Gents to retrieve my clothing. But to my
horror they had gone. I searched the pub,
asked behind the bar and pleaded with
Debbie's friends to stop their fun and
lend me a pair of trousers. But
having been the
instrument of
her humiliation,
Debbie took
great delight
in my
predicament.

'What are you going to do?'
she giggled. There was only
one thing I could do. I left the
pub and made my way to the tube
station as discreetly as possible. Travelling
on the Bakerloo Line is an ordeal at the best of
times, but the embarrassment of that particular
journey will stay with me forever. My loin-cloth
was damp with perspiration as I finally trudged
up the stairs towards my squalid attic. As I
fumbled for my Chubb I became aware of a
shadowy figure behind me. I swung round to
confront this mysterious intruder and saw to my
horror, emerging from the gloom, Mr Bishop in
a rhino-skin bikini. His eyes glinted with excitement as
his full-length Dorothy Lamour wig cascaded over his
hairy shoulders.

It looked like I had picked the wrong night to
come home dressed as Tarzan.

Fanny meanwhile had matured into a sleek
and graceful creature. Pert and intelligent,
people would stop us in the street to stroke her
and utter words of admiration. And her attraction for
other dogs was soon to take on another and more serious
dimension (hormones being what they are). Walking a dog
on heat is never easy and wasn't helped in Fanny's case because
she insisted on approaching dogs backwards. She wanted to get
straight down to the nitty gritty. Many a wheel barrow has had a very
nasty surprise. In fact there is a gardener in Regent's Park who will
never feel the same about Dahlias. I was shocked by her wanton
behaviour. Whenever we returned from the park there would
be at least fifteen other dogs in attendance. It was a bit like
squeezing Linda Lusardi into a wet T-shirt and taking her
down the barracks. Fanny's frustration reached boiling
point – she had a one-track mind. Even the
furry cushion cover was a potential lover;
she would flirt with it coquettishly, giving
it the come on and then giving it the get off.
But pregnancy for either of us in our
wretched domestic circumstances
would have been reckless.

It was my custom to take
a hot bath every afternoon,
leaving Fanny alone in the room. And
it was while I was enjoying one such soak that
the deviousness of lust manifested itself.
When I returned to my room I was
horrified to see that the sheets
had been crudely knotted together
and Fanny had shimmied down to street
level. I rushed to the window, fearful
of what I might see. Below, in full
view of the neighbours, a sordid
tableau was being enacted. I cannot
bring myself to describe the activity
I witnessed (but it wasn't pavement
drawing).*

FANNY: AS SOON AS JULIAN HAD LEFT THE ROOM WITH HIS BATH TOWEL AND WASH BAG
I HEARD A GRUFF, GUTTERAL SERENADE FROM THE STREET BELOW. I INSTINCTIVELY
KNEW THIS TO BE THE PERFECT SPECIMEN OF CANINE MASCULINITY THAT I HAD FIRST
NOTICED IN THE PARK THE DAY BEFORE. WHAT WAS I TO DO? MY HEART BEAT FURIOUSLY
WITHIN MY BREAST. I WANTED HIM AS MUCH AS HE WANTED ME. THE THOUGHT OF HIS
SHAFT OF LOVE QUIVERING WITHIN ME EXCITED ME TILL I COULD NO LONGER WALK
PROPERLY. DON'T ASK ME HOW BUT I QUICKLY KNOTTED SOME SHEETS TOGETHER. I
TIED ONE END TO THE BED-POST AND SWIFTLY CLAMBERED DOWN TO THE PAVEMENT.

'WHAT IS YOUR NAME?' I SOBBED, SHAKING WITH AN ANIMAL LUST THAT I COULD
NOT BEGIN TO COMPREHEND.

'MR BISHOP,' HE SAID, 'AND WHAT'S MORE YOU AIN'T NO CACTUS.'

Unfortunately Fanny's first experience did not satisfy her. Soon she became known as the neighbourhood tart. It seemed that every dog within a five-mile radius made the journey to our front door and Fanny saw to it that every one of them went home with a smile on his face. Her sexual appetite was voracious – she even placed a card in the newsagent window. Not for her the cheap innuendo of 'French lessons given', her advertisement simply read 'Free sex'.

But such reckless behaviour couldn't go on forever and it was no surprise when she became pregnant. In a matter of weeks her hour-glass figure had expanded to the size of a Ford Cortina. Her gambol had become a waddle. The slightest exertion would leave her panting, and she developed strange cravings for weird and wonderful foods. I was forever getting up in the night to fetch her rollmop herrings and powdered egg. And suddenly she became very keen on German Art films and Murray Mints.

I was determined that this pregnancy should be trouble-free. I read all the available literature, *A Tale of Two Cities*, *Teach Yourself Trigonometry*, *The Prime of Miss Jean Brodie*, but there was nothing about pregnant dogs in any of them. A trip to the library was in order. I left Fanny in front of the fire, happily chomping her way through half a pound of Murray Mints and watching her favourite German Art movie *Hans Drops His Trousers*. *

HANS DROPS HIS TROUSERS IS SET IN PRE-WAR BERLIN. THE TROUSERS OBVIOUSLY REPRESENT THE WEIMAR REPUBLIC AND THE VERY FACT THAT HANS DROPS THEM IS INDICATIVE OF THE MIDDLE CLASS' REJECTION OF HINDENBURG'S ECONOMIC POLICY. UNDOUBTEDLY THE UNDERPANTS SYMBOLISE THE EMERGENCE OF NATIONAL SOCIALISM. THE OUTLINE OF HIS SEXUAL ORGANS CLEARLY PREDICTS THE CONSTRUCTION OF THE AUTOBAHNS. PREVIOUSLY RELEASED UNDER THE TITLE *SHOW US YOUR ARSE, SQUARE HEAD*, THIS EPIC WORK CAPTURES PERFECTLY THE MOOD OF DECADENCE ONLY HINTED AT IN THE EARLIER MOVIE *WATCH OUT GUSTAV, THERE'S A HOMOSEXUAL BEHIND YOU*. 'HIGHLY RECOMMENDED' *Time Out*.

At the time I was living in an area under the control of a fervently right-wing council. Hangings were compulsory for driving offences and their policy was so anti-gay that anyone with a mere hint of a lisp was shot dead in the streets. I arrived at the library just in time to witness the monthly book-burning ritual. Any book that promoted homosexuality in their eyes was destined for the bonfire. This included such works as *The Two Gentlemen of Verona*, *Scouting for Boys* and *Lord of the Flies*. As a result of such rabid culling, the shelves were now sparsely populated. Even the books that remained had been heavily censored. Council employees with scissors and Tipp-ex at the ready would scout every page of every book deleting any passages where one man was found to be talking to another.

The day-to-day running of the library was in the hands of Miss Crogan, who governed her silent domain with icy authority. She had very strict views and firmly believed it was her duty to stamp out enjoyment wherever it raised its pleasantly tousled head. She eyed me suspiciously as I browsed through the Pet Care section. There was something about my walk she didn't like and when I approached her counter with a copy of *Doggy Up The Spout* by the Duchess of York,* I glimpsed the vague outline of a crossbow beneath her pleated skirt. She viciously date-stamped the book and threw it back at me with such force that I was bent double with pain. Later that night, still somewhat miffed, I burnt down the library.

*DOGGY UP THE SPOUT WAS A GRIPPING READ ALTHOUGH THE ROYAL PHRASEOLOGY WAS IRRITATING. MOST PROBLEMS WERE DEALT WITH SIMPLY BY SAYING 'GET THE SERVANTS TO SORT THIS ONE OUT'.

Caring for Fanny as she neared her time became a twenty-four-hour occupation and I had to hand in my notice at the 'Get 'Em Off' Singing Telegram Agency. I spent my time mopping her brow and preparing the four sumptuous meals a day she required. She was now so big she was actually larger than the room we were living in. And as the days turned to weeks I thought the puppies would never arrive. I considered sending in a search party; it seemed I was shovelling food into one end of Fanny and getting nothing worthwhile out of the other. In a desperate attempt to coax her offspring into the world I lifted Fanny's tail and rattled a biscuit tin. Still nothing. With a sigh I placed the tin back on the shelf. No sooner had I turned away than I heard a squelch and a whimper. I spun around in amazement and, unbelievable as it may be, saw Fanny softly nuzzling four new-born puppies.*

I couldn't afford champagne with which to wet the puppies' heads so I opened a bottle of bleach and gave the toilet a good scrub out.

*I DON'T KNOW WHY I CALL THIS UNBELIEVABLE. WHAT DID I EXPECT TO SEE WHEN I SPUN ROUND? A NAKED FRANK MUIR, SPREAD-EAGLED ACROSS A FORK-LIFT TRUCK?

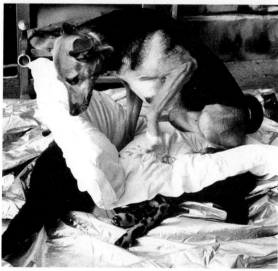

I christened the new additions to our happy household Wesley, Harriet, Emma and Margaret; one dog and three bitches. Or, as Fanny referred to them, four bastards.

Perhaps Fanny did love her off-spring, but when I caught her trying to smother the little darlings with a pillow I made an anonymous call to the Social Services. Of course she was all sweetness and light when the inspector arrived – teets all round for the pups and a large scotch for him. No sooner was he out of the door than she kicked Emma under the wardrobe and clouted the other three with a Bonio. She was a brusque and matronly mother; *spare the rod, spoil the litter* was her motto. She encouraged her pups to be independent from an early age. When they were only a few days old she took them out for a ride on the underground and returned home alone. How they made their way back from Gants Hill with their eyes still shut, I shall never know. Science tells us that dogs have a highly developed sense of smell and perhaps they caught a whiff of Mr Bishop's creosote. Her competence as a mother was frankly dubious, and often I was reminded of Faye Dunaway's portrayal of Joan Crawford in *Mommie Dearest*. The resemblance was uncanny *and* unnatural. Not only were Fanny's eyebrows the same, she also displayed a complete inability to act.

She would spend a large part of her day gazing longingly out of the window. Was she regretting her wham-bam-thank-you-Fido days of reckless promiscuity? Was she hankering for the wide open spaces, the streets, the parks, and the woodlands? Or can we say with the benefit of hindsight that she was beginning to reach out beyond vale and meadow, into the strange and alien world of show business. Did she have something to convey to the riff-raff at large, did she have something to bark about?

CHAPTER FOUR

FAREWELL FALLOPIANS, HELLO LEICESTER SQUARE

'HOLD THE FORT FOR I AM COMING.' PHILIPP BLISS, 'THE CHARM'.

Once the puppies had been found good theatrical homes, life returned to some kind of normality for Fanny and I. A quick trip to the vet ensured there would be no more puppies. From now on she was a career dog with a ruthless ambition appropriate for the cut-throat world of show business. She was determined to get to the top and nobody, not even Gyles Brandreth, would stand in her way. She became an avid viewer of all light entertainment television programmes, endlessly studying videos of the presenters. Among her favourites was Mike Smith. How did he do it? And why? And could she ever hope to match the suave sophistication of Jim Bowen on *Bullseye*? Only time would tell. She was stranded at the bottom of the ladder – years of hard slog lay ahead of her – but she had a dream.

However the practical side of the operation was left entirely up to me. While Fanny stayed at home dreaming of rubbing shoulders with Mavis Nicholson and Noel Edmonds, I was rummaging through the 50p rail at Oxfam, searching for a suitable costume for our stage debut. I had a booking at the Earth Exchange Cabaret the following Monday and my stage name was to be Gillian Pie Face.*

*THIS CURIOUS NAME REQUIRES SOME EXPLANATION. IN THE 1830S MY GREAT, GREAT, GREAT AUNT GILLIAN ELOPED WITH A PIE FACE AGAINST THE EXPRESS WISHES OF HER FATHER, THE VERY REVEREND EBENEZER GREENHALGH. THE REVEREND, IN A FIT OF PIQUE, VOWED THAT NO PIE FACE WOULD EVER AGAIN BE WELCOME AT THE VICARAGE AND SO BEGAN A FEUD THAT WAS TO CAST A SINISTER SHADOW OVER THE GENERATIONS THAT FOLLOWED. QUITE WHY HE CONSIDERED THE PIE FACES SO ENTIRELY UNSUITABLE A MATCH FOR HIS DAUGHTER IS IMPOSSIBLE TO SAY, BUT MY GRANDMOTHER SOMETIMES MUTTERED DARKLY ABOUT 'REAL BASTARDS'.
GILLIAN AND HER NEW HUSBAND, HUGO PIE FACE, EMBARKED ON A TERRIBLE CAMPAIGN OF REVENGE AGAINST THE REVEREND GREENHALGH. AT FIRST THIS CONSISTED OF SHOUTING 'FAT BUM' THROUGH HIS LETTERBOX, BUT IT SWIFTLY PROGRESSED TO DISRUPTING CHURCH SERVICES WITH LOUD RENDITIONS OF THE BAWDY SONG 'GET OFF THE TABLE MABLE, THE MONEY'S FOR THE BEER'. THE FEUD ESCALATED FURTHER WHEN IN 1862 PETER PIE FACE, A CONFIRMED BACHELOR, SET UP HOME WITH A MAN CALLED BINKY. ONE EVENING, AFTER DRINKING TOO MUCH ELDERBERRY WINE, THE MERRY PAIR CALLED AT THE VICARAGE AND IN A DRUNKEN SLUR DEMANDED THAT THE DECREPIT REVEREND MARRY THEM. THIS WAS TOO MUCH FOR THE OLD MAN'S HEART AND HE FELL FACE FIRST INTO THE FONT. MATTERS WERE MADE WORSE WHEN BINKY TURNED UP AT THE FUNERAL AND KEPT WINKING AT THE ORGANIST.
ALTHOUGH THERE IS NOT A DROP OF PIE FACE BLOOD IN MY VEINS, I CANNOT FAIL TO SEE RED WHEN I CROSS THE PATH OF A DASTARDLY GREENHALGH.

Monday soon came. Resplendent in kaftan and wig, I waited nervously in the wings as Kim Wells, resident compère at the Earth Exchange Cabaret, introduced me.

'And now, ladies and gentlemen, something a little bit different ... would you welcome Gillian Pie Face and Fanny the Dog!' As the splattering of applause indicated, there weren't many punters in that night. I stood before them nervously, my mind suddenly a blank.

'Hello,' I stammered. *'This is my dog Fanny. Do you think she is nice?'* The silence that ensued was interrupted only by the sound of my underpants filling up. Fanny glared at me disapprovingly. I was letting us both down. After five minutes of this humiliation with not a laugh in sight, Kim signalled from the wings that it was time for me to leave the stage. As I did so he gave me a sympathetic pat on the shoulder and said, *'You will never work again.'*

That night, after throwing my underpants into the canal, I cried myself to sleep. I spent the next day deep in thought. Clearly the road to stardom was a rocky one. Where was the camaraderie? Where were the drugs and the groupies?

But then, I consoled myself, I was lucky to have one friend in the world. I turned away from the window for a moment and gazed down at Fanny, curled up in front of the fire. She too seemed to be preoccupied; perhaps she was thinking about how lucky she was to have me. Suddenly a curious thing happened. Fanny reached under her basket and picked up a piece of paper with her teeth. She dropped the paper in my lap and returned to her basket. It was almost as if she was trying to communicate. I idly turned the paper over and was astonished to read in shaky red biro,

'I want to go solo.'

The cabaret scene in those days was a small and closely knit community. Within days, news of my pitiful attempt at comedy had become legend. Muffled laughs would greet my tremulous request for work and sometimes the phone would go dead in mid-snigger. My career was over before it had begun.

I sought advice from those acts that had already established themselves on the cabaret circuit. A fresh-faced Ben Elton gave me an excellent tip which I treasure to this day (although I have never actually taken any notice of it):
'Think fast, talk fast, get on fast, get off fast, go home fast, sleep fast, eat breakfast.'

Santini, the legendary left-wing hypnotist, told me that his success was entirely due to alcohol. He never actually hypnotised his victims, he just breathed on them. *Always be more pissed than your audience* was his motto. It was an incredible act to see. He would sway on to the stage, burping and hiccuping with a mesmerising regularity. Waving his hip-flask at the audience, he would constantly repeat his hilarious catchphrase *'Where am I?'*

But the best piece of advice that I received in those dark and doomy days was from a woman called Doris, who had retired from the stage many years before. *'Never give up,'* she said. I tried to keep my pecker up with bits of string but it drooped in the face of constant rejection.

After weeks of trying still nobody would book me. Just as I was about to throw in the towel and ask the brick-layer down the road if he needed a hod carrier, fate stepped in and offered me a second chance.

The woman who usually booked the acts at a thriving pub venue called The Fox and Egg Cup was away the day I phoned pleading for work and her friend, who hadn't heard about the Earth Exchange debacle, agreed to give me a booking that very night. I hoped and prayed that this time it would be different. I knew it was make or break time, but somehow I felt that tonight was going to be our night.

Fanny danced about the flat in a state of some excitement. I quickly ran the iron over my kaftan and dowsed my curly blond wig in talcum powder. The Fox and Egg Cup was packed to the rafters that night, Santini was on the bill* and the atmosphere was electric. In the cramped dressing room Fanny and I tried to keep ourselves to ourselves but it wasn't easy. Apart from Santini there was the compère Tom Lloyd and a six-piece *a cappella* troupe called Give Us Our Equity Cards. They were on first.

Tom Lloyd kicked the evening off with his crowd-pleasing impressions of various famous people farting in the bath,

before introducing Give Us Our Equity Cards. The audience was unimpressed and slowly drifted to the bar. The hum of conversation grew steadily louder as the six tone-deaf drama students struggled through their set.

'I think it went rather well,' said one of them as they returned to the dressing room. By this time Tom was back on stage doing his impressions of famous people eating a piece of Ryvita. They weren't an easy crowd to please, but his Robert Morley brought the house down as always.

AND ON THE BRANDY.

By the time I was announced conditions were perfect. We made our entrance to a healthy round of applause. As I stood on that stage I knew the time was right.

The audience hated me.

I was heckled relentlessly, Fanny was ridiculed and even my kaftan was a target for snidy comments. I tried to retaliate but all I could come up with was *'Sticks and stones may break my bones but words will never hurt me.'* This comment back-fired when the audience started throwing sticks and stones. To add insult to injury Fanny began fetching the sticks and returning them to the people who were throwing them. This meant the barrage continued for over an hour and it wasn't until Santini took to the stage that order was restored.

I sat in the dressing room unable to understand where I had gone wrong. Tom Lloyd offered few crumbs of comfort. *'Comedy is a tricky business. There is only one way to get a laugh in my experience and that is to do impressions of famous people.'*

As I left the pub that night, clutching my hard-earned fifteen pounds, I heard Tom winding up the evening with his impression of Noel Gordon hailing a taxi. In my heart I knew there must be another way. Fanny and I wandered aimlessly for a while until we found ourselves in Leicester Square. The screeching starlings, the gaudy neon lights, the touts, the tramps, the tourists, the half-price ticket booths, the mounds of litter, a thousand plastic penguins sliding down a thousand plastic slides, the lost, the homeless, the dirty all combined in a swirling nightmare of noise and confusion. I clutched Fanny to me as I staggered through the madness. This was hell and everyone was damned. So much for show business.

CHAPTER FIVE

CHUMPLESS AND PROUD

'MY BELOVED PUT IN HIS HAND BY THE HOLE OF THE DOOR, AND MY BOWELS WERE MOVED FOR HIM.' THE OLD TESTAMENT.

Spreading the word of my particular brand of whimsy was clearly a more difficult task than I had previously assumed it to be. I took some comfort in the fact that Van Gogh only sold two paintings in the whole of his life, yet now he is hailed as a genius. But then he was off his chump, and perhaps I was heading that way myself. Was I to be a chumpless wonder like so many great artists this world has thrown up then hurled against the rocks of artistic endeavour?

I withdrew from the outside world. The harshness of reality was too much for me and I rarely left my room. But domestic contentment was not to be mine either, a new tenant moved into the room directly below mine. She wasted no time in introducing herself and telling me a bit about her history.

*'My name is
Wendy Bucket,
right? Just moved
in downstairs, right?'*
She was a burly woman
with a face like a bag of
spanners. Her manner could
best be described as aggressive:

she made a hammerhead shark look like Russell Grant.

'I sleep with an electric stungun under my pillow and I am not afraid to use it. I got banged up when I was thirteen. Forgot my PE kit, right? Didn't want to get into trouble with the gym teacher, right? So I smashed her head in with a hockey stick. They only caught me 'cause I had her brains in my pocket.'

With that she laughed as if she had made some kind of joke and I made a mental note never to marry her.

I tried to keep myself to myself and ignored the terrified screams that emanated from her flat every Saturday night. Her boyfriend was an Hell's Angel called Derek, but he belonged to an obscure chapter called the Night Nurses. Discarding the traditional black leather garb, these lads wore white starched nurses uniforms. They took their code of conduct and their ethos directly from the National Health Service. Anyone who crossed their path was likely to have their temperature taken or their blood pressure read. They would cruise about town late at night, horribly brisk and cheerful, descending on innocent passers-by with their shrill war-cry:

'Come along now, there is a lot of people worse off than you!'

Tumbling them into the back of a make-shift ambulance, they would make appointments for them to see specialists and then cancel them at the last minute. Some unfortunate victims were dragged back to Wendy Bucket's flat and much against their will were kept in over night for observation. And as for the screams that I heard every Saturday night . . . Perhaps they were the result of over-zealous pillow plumping.

Miss Bucket's unwanted visitations continued. She would knock on my door and make unreasonable demands: *'Turn your fridge down, right? I can't sleep. My boyfriend has got someone in intensive care.'* Not wishing to stir up trouble with the neighbours, I disconnected my fridge, but this didn't satisfy her. On another occasion she knocked on my door to complain about the noise of the traffic outside. When I told her it wasn't my fault she said she knew for a fact I was doing it deliberately and unless I re-routed the juggernauts, I would be given a blanket bath I'd never forget. I wrote to the Ministry of Transport explaining my position and luckily they acceded to my request.

Miss Bucket's persecution only added to my gloom and despondency. Even my attempt to escape into seclusion had been a disaster. Fate and reality conspired together to push me to the very brink of the abyss. In my darkest hour I contemplated ending it all. But how was I to do the deed? I couldn't bear the idea of suffering and pain, so my journey to the great behind had to be swift and easy. This ruled out cutting my head off with an electric saw. And vanity precluded any means of departing this life that would result in disfigurement. I decided to eat myself to death. On one of my rare forays into the outside world I purchased one hundred and thirty saveloys from the fish and chip shop. If I was going to die, I might as well have something hot inside me. Back home, with the saveloys warming in the oven, I composed my farewell note.

To whom it may concern.

By the time you read this I will have found what I set out to find —
Death by Saveloy.

It is a well-known fact that one dodgy saveloy from the Old Kent Road is enough to finish you off, but I have had a hundred and thirty so there is no hope for me.

Signed.
A lonely desperate soul.

I sealed
the envelope and
placed it on the mantel-
piece, then sat in front
of the fire and
began my fatal
meal. At first I
found it difficult
to eat more than
one or two but
after thirty I
began to hit
my stride. Saveloy
after saveloy dis-
appeared into my
cavernous maw. As
I quivered at the
prospect of my
fifty-fourth saveloy
in as many min-
utes, I suddenly
became aware of
another presence.
I glanced down at
Fanny who was
staring intently
into the middle
distance, wagging
her tail as if she
was about to greet
a very old friend.
As I followed her
line of vision I
noticed a curious
haze in the centre
of the room. As I
continued to stare
at it the haze
became a recog-
nisably human
shape. It was a
middle-aged man wear-
ing a loud striped suit
and a trilby.

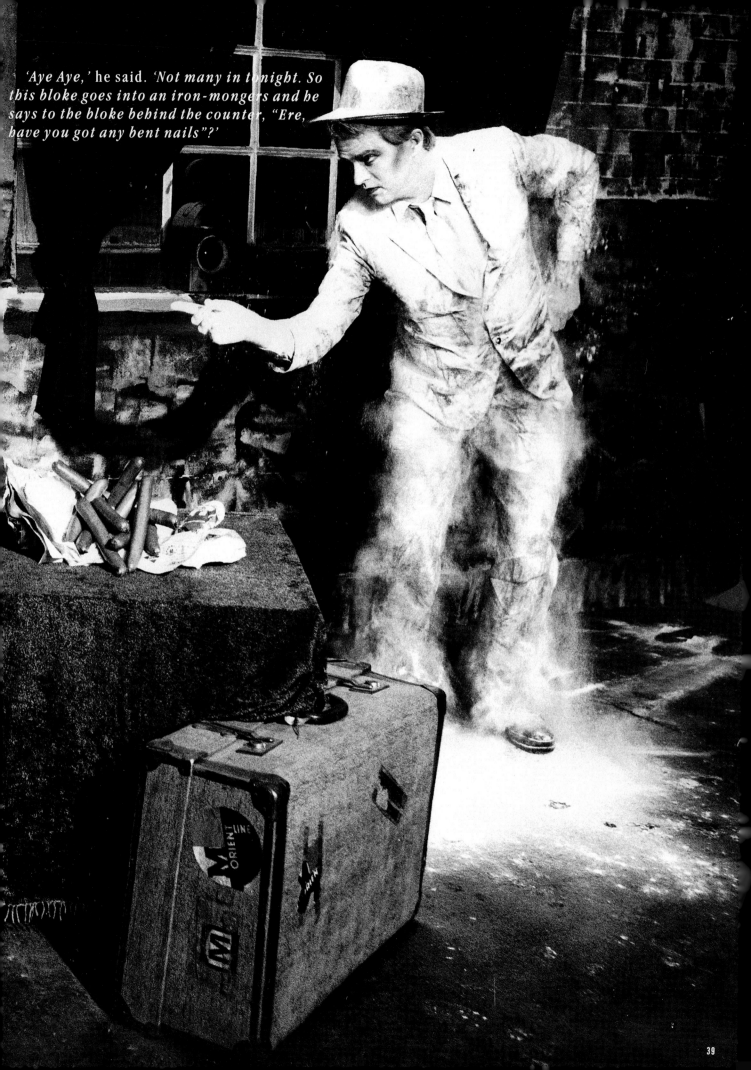

'Aye Aye,' he said. 'Not many in tonight. So this bloke goes into an iron-mongers and he says to the bloke behind the counter, "Ere, have you got any bent nails"?'

As the apparition continued with this comic monologue I quite forgot the misery of my circumstances and began to heckle. I found the punchline of his bent nail story somewhat offensive and I told him so.

'Now then, now then,' he responded. 'No heckling please, the man has got a job to do.'

'I shall say what I like in my own room,' I said, affronted by his presumptous manner. 'Stop telling these ridiculous stories and tell me what you're doing here.'

'Ernie Moss is the name and comedy is the game,' he replied, doffing his trilby.

'And what do you want?' I said with all the authority that a homosexual full of saveloys could muster.

'I am from the Variety wing of the spirit world, I have been dead since 1946 and I have come to tell you the secret of comedy.'

'I don't want to know,' I said, my cheeks flushing at the very mention of comedy.

'Hear me out, hear me out. We've been watching you and you have been making every mistake in the book. There are rules of comedy, you see, it's just like any line of business, you have got to learn the ropes.'

'What rules?' I said, biting into saveloy number fifty-four.

'Rule number one,' he said, 'never work on a Tuesday. Tuesday isn't a funny day of the week. Rule number two: if you are going to use irony, never employ it in a room holding more than three hundred people. Rule number three: rice pudding is over-estimated as a source of comedy. Rule number four: never begin a joke with the word "yesterday", it doesn't work. I once saw an act begin with "Yesterday I ate a rice pudding" and they found him two days later floating face down in the Thames. By then it was Thursday.' He paused for breath and I realised that in his own simple, kind-hearted way he was talking rubbish. But I thought to myself, if this old fool can earn a living in show business, then so can I. Half an hour later he was up to rule five hundred and sixty-eight.

'Don't take the piss out of bananas. They can't answer back.'

'Thank you very much,' I interrupted.
'I get the picture.'

'Fair do's,' he said. *'I won't outstay my welcome. But remember, I am always here if you need me,'* and with that he disappeared into a thin plume of smoke.

The decision as to whether or not I should continue with my suicide bid had already been made by Fanny. She had eaten the rest of the saveloys and now sat burping contentedly by the fire.

After this paranormal visitation I found myself in a state of wonder, rather like Doris Stokes must have felt after Elvis Presley had whispered up her earhole. I lay down on my bed and went into a spontaneous re-birthing experience.
An hour and twenty minutes later I emerged refreshed and full of inner peace –

I felt like a new man.*

*BUT WHERE WOULD I FIND ONE AT THAT TIME OF NIGHT?

The phone rang. It was Kim Wells from the Earth Exchange and what he had to say astonished me.

'I just had a call from a bloke called Ernie Moss. He was raving about you, said you were the best thing since Wilson, Kepple and Betty. I've never heard of them, but that is good enough for me. Now I know the last time you were here you were crap. And I have also heard on the grapevine that you were crap at the Fox and Egg Cup. But the way I look at it is, there is no way you can be crap three times in a row. Come down next Monday.'

I went down the next Monday and I was crap.

'You were crap,' said Kim. *'Who'd of thought you would be crap three times in a row! I tell you what, come down next Monday because never in my whole life have I ever seen anyone be crap four times in a row.'* I went down the next Monday and I was crap again.

'Well, that's a record as far as I am concerned,' said Kim, shaking his head. *'Crap, crap, crap, crap! I daren't put you on again as I've had death threats . . . but I'll tell you what, you have a nice face, so I'll give you one more chance. Call me crazy, call me a fool, call me a crazy fool, but I'll tell you this for nothing, if you're crap next Monday you have got to promise me, for your own sake, that you will give up.'* I nodded in agreement.

The next week I spent every minute of every day working on the act. I honed and polished* and had several visits from Ernie Moss who gave me this invaluable advice. *'Always remember this: "Never let the audience see you using a hair brush, they'll lose all respect for you".'*

When Monday came around I was imbued with a new sense of confidence. I sparkled as I walked on to that stage. I was crap. I found Kim collapsed in a corner. *'Five times,'* he kept muttering. *'He was crap five times in a row.'*

'I'll see you next week, shall I?' I enquired hopefully. His only answer was to sob gently into a handkerchief.

I took this as a maybe.

*IN THE MORNINGS I POLISHED AND IN THE AFTERNOONS I HONED.

42

CHAPTER SIX

A FOOT IN THE DOOR

'ART IS THE MATHEMATICAL RESULT OF THE EMOTIONAL DESIRE FOR BEAUTY.' OSCAR WILDE.

I began to think that perhaps it wasn't just me, perhaps it was the venue that was crap. It wasn't the right setting for Gillian Pie Face. But then what was? At that stage of my career I was hardly in a position to dictate the colour of the curtains. My next engagement was at a polytechnic in West London. My first problem that night was trying to get Fanny into the building.

'You can't bring that dog in 'ere son,' said the uniformed guard at the Porters' Lodge.

'She's part of the cabaret act,' I said.

'I don't care what she is. No dogs allowed on the premises.' Clearly my lack of subservience was making this little man twitch. *'I'm wearing a uniform and you're not. I'm here to maintain the rules and regulations and you're here to break them. I'm on one side of the fence and you're on the other. I'm a right-wing fascist and you're a commie bastard. I'm a happily married man and you're the spawn of Beelzebub. Well, when I say I'm a happily married man, I mean I've got three miserable teenage kids at home who sit around all day watching soap operas and drawing on the walls with felt tip pen and I've got a wife whose idea of sexual activity is watching BBC2. The only pleasure I get from family life is the knowledge that millions of others are just as miserable as I am – and you think you're getting past me with that dog?'*

'Well, eventually, yes,' I said.

'Don't get me wrong, son. I'm not refusing you entry because I don't like the look of you. And I'm not refusing you entry because rule fourteen, subsection four, clearly states "No dogs allowed on the premises". I'm refusing you entry because I love you . . . I want to be with you . . . I want to share those precious moments. I want candle-lit dinners in over-priced restaurants where the bill is taken care of by a small bit of plastic. I want —'

'You want seeing to,' I said, brushing past him with Fanny into the Student Union Hall where the cabaret was to take place.

I met the social secretary and he led me down a long series of corridors. 'Here's your dressing room,' he said, flinging open a door and showing me the car park. 'The bar don't shut till eleven, so you'll be on about eleven-thirty, after the band and before the disco.'

'What's the band?' I said.

'Satan's Slippers,' he replied. 'A heavy metal band that worship the devil and sensible footwear, they believe in eternal damnation but see no reason why it shouldn't be cosy.'

I set out my make-up on the bonnet of a Volkswagen Polo and ran quickly through my lines. Once the band had stomped through their set in foam-soled slippers I was announced over a crackling PA and took the stage to ear-piercing screeches of feedback. The audience was extremely drunk and I looked out on a sea of horizontal bodies and vomit. Cider was five pence a pint and any student who drank more than six pints was given a free filofax and a plastic liver. Consequently my subtle brand of humour wasn't going down too well.

Fanny curled her lip in disdain and it was time for desperate measures. I'd had just about enough of their insults when one spotty faced oik with half a pound of Clearasil on his face stood up and screamed, *'Which one is the dog?'* My blood boiled and I decided to make an example of the young lout. Fixing him firmly in my stare, I said, *'And who cuts your hair for you? Is it the council?'* The room erupted with laughter and even those who were unconscious raised a smile. I hit him with another right between the eyes. *'Men like you don't grow on trees do they? They usually swing from them.'*

The applause rang in my ears as I left the stage that night. It had been a triumph. Perspiration trickled down my kaftan as I quickly changed into my day-wear. The social secretary seemed genuinely pleased as he paid me my money, and Fanny and I were truly happy as we made our way to the exit. Stepping nimbly over the bodies of several dozen cider-soaked students, I realised that I'd reached a turning point.

Bookings began to trickle in – Gillian Pie Face was getting out and about. Fanny was happier than she had been for months.

But I *still* didn't have a girlfriend.*

*LET'S FACE IT, I DIDN'T WANT ONE. WHY THIS PRETENCE? IS IT MERELY TO TEASE THE FEMALE READER? OH SHAME ON ME, WHY CAN'T I LET THE WORLD SEE ME AS I AM? WHY DO I KEEP UP THIS FAÇADE OF HETEROSEXUALITY? THERE IS NO WIFE AND KIDS LIVING IN BROMLEY. THAT INTERVIEW I DID WITH THE *TV TIMES* WAS A FARCE; THE WORDS TURNED TO CARDBOARD IN MY MOUTH EVEN AS I SPOKE THEM. MY LOVELY WIFE UNA, PHOTOGRAPHED WITH THE LITTLE ONES IN HER DREAM KITCHEN, WAS NONE OTHER THAN MY FRIEND CRAIG IN A PINNY.

CHAPTER SEVEN

FORE-ARM UP THE CHIMNEY

'THE WORLD CONTINUES TO OFFER
GLITTERING PRIZES TO THOSE WHO HAVE
STONE HEARTS AND SHARP SWORDS.'
FREDERICK EDWYN SMITH,
EARL OF BIRKENHEAD.

I began to feel more confident. There were aspects of the act that clearly appealed to people. After a show the performers would gather around the bar discussing the ins and outs of the business, and often our subject was the intricate nature of comic technique.

Peter Warren would often lead these impromptu debates. Having been to Cambridge he knew more about comedy than any other man alive. He had invented an extensive glossary of phrases to describe each and every comic device. For example, a 'timebomb' is the pay-off or punchline for a joke set up some time earlier. A 'slap-back' is a combination of a pun and a somersault. But he himself was most adept at the so-called 'man-hole cover'. This was the term used for a concealed joke. The joke was set up but the punchline was deliberately hidden from the audience. Punters would go home bemused, wondering if they had missed something, as indeed they had. A true 'man-hole cover' practitioner would probably leave the stage after twenty minutes without getting a single laugh. For him, it was a matter of honour. Lesser comedians would gather around, patting him on the back, whispering in wonderment, *'I counted seventeen man-hole covers, one after the other!'* or even, *'I thought he was going to lose it when that woman in the front row nearly giggled.'* As his act has grown more sophisticated over the years, his man-hole covers have become so devious that even seasoned comedians can't spot the jokes. In my opinion, he is a genius.

It was not uncommon for these after-show drinks to develop into a late night revel. I sometimes wondered what Fanny made of all the hubbub as she sat serenely on a bar stool, casting disdainful glances about her.*

*FANNY: I DESIRED THE GLAMOUR AND EXCITEMENT OF HOLLYWOOD, NOT THE SEEDY REALITY OF CRICKLEWOOD. IT WAS ALL VERY WELL FOR JULIAN TO FLIT ACROSS THE BEER-STAINED CARPET, CHIRPING MERRILY WITH THESE PEOPLE, BUT HE HAD, LET'S FACE IT, SPENT MOST OF HIS LIFE AS A SOCIAL OUTCAST, AND HE WOULD TAKE ANY CRUMBS OF FRIENDSHIP, HOWEVER UNSAVOURY. I WOULD CLOSE MY EYES AND IMAGINE A BETTER WORLD FOR BOTH OF US. THE MODICUM OF SUCCESS THAT WE WERE NOW BEGINNING TO SHARE WAS JUST THE START. AN INEBRIATED SANTINI MIGHT BELCH IN MY EAR BUT ALTHOUGH I WANTED TO GROWL AT THE DRUNKEN IDIOT, I JUST SIMPERED SWEETLY. FOR THE MOMENT, SANTINI WAS A USEFUL CONTACT, AND I COULD NOT LET MY TRUE FEELINGS SHOW.

On one such occasion, backstage at the Horse and Bucket, a golden opportunity presented itself. I was busy packing away my make-up bag when I felt a tap on the shoulder. *'Allow me to introduce myself, young man. My name is Kingsley St Claire, of St Claire's Artistes. I represent all the big names in this business. And if I don't represent them, they are not in this business.'*

I turned to see a well-groomed man of about fifty-one. He was wearing a camel hair coat with a sable-trimmed collar. He looked so much the part I couldn't understand why he wasn't smoking a large cigar. I shook the hand that he offered me, and asked him what he wanted.

He replied, *'I caught the act and I loved it. You're new, you're different, you're exciting. But one word of advice: you should do your act in the nude, it's crying out for it. All my acts work in the nude. King of the nudies they call me.'*

'Well, I don't think —' I began.

'*Go on, strip off now! Don't think about it, just peel 'em! That's how Anita Harris started. When she sang her first hit record on* Top of the Pops *she was starkers. People don't remember that now. Once you're established, of course, you can wear what you like. Look at that Perry Como – for the past five years he has been voted the Best Dressed Man in show business, but for the first fifteen years of his career he was known as "show us your bum" Como. Now I don't want to raise your hopes, but I think you could be another Perry. In the name of show business, drop your trousers.*'

'*But I have a rather unsightly appendix scar,*' I protested.

'*Never mind that! Now the dog has got the right idea, not a stitch on. She doesn't do anything. All she does is sit there during the act. But she's naked. So people can't keep their eyes off her. You just look out of place wearing all those clothes. People think there's something funny about you.*'

'*But I like wearing my kaftan,*' I said, astonished.

'*Fair enough, I'm not trying to bulldoze you. Here is my card, have a think about it and give us a ring.*' And with that he lit a fat cigar and wandered off.

I thought it only polite to phone a few days later. He pleaded with me to send him a polaroid of my behind. The idea was tempting. Money was still scarce and I was hardly working every night of the week, but to take up such an offer, I felt, would be detrimental to my higher comic aspirations. Bums are only funny to school boys. Spare me such sordid attempts at humour.

I was beginning to understand that the world of show business was a mixture of both delightful and dangerous personalities. Kingsley St Claire was simply one of the less dangerous sharks that I was to encounter.

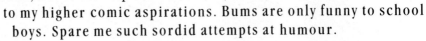

CHAPTER EIGHT

DON'T MIND ME. I'M ONLY MINCING

'THE FICKLENESS OF THE WOMEN I LOVE
IS ONLY EQUALLED BY THE INFERNAL
CONSTANCY OF THE WOMEN WHO
LOVE ME.' GEORGE BERNARD SHAW,
'THE PHILANDERER', ACT II.

Meanwhile our domestic situation had become intolerable. Fanny's romp with Mr Bishop in the street had not been forgotten, and because she was no longer willing to continue this sordid liaison he gave us notice to quit. Actually, I felt it was time to move on anyway. In the room below mine Wendy Bucket and her boyfriend had greatly expanded their medical activities. They had now progressed from pillow plumping to internal probes, and while the former may be safely attempted by the committed amateur, lunging at an orifice with a torch and a knitting needle may cause considerable distress to the patient (particularly if they are waiting for a bus at the time).

Living upstairs from such gruesome goings-on was beginning to affect my sanity. I began to scout around for alternative living arrangements. People tell you that it is impossible to find good accommodation in Central London. What rot! On the first day of looking I found five perfectly decent flats. Unfortunately none of them were for rent or sale, but they were there nevertheless.

For some years I had been
on the waiting list of a housing
co-operative. I was tired of aggressive
landlords and troublesome neighbours and wanted to live as part of a supportive and caring community.
I wanted to borrow a cup of sugar from my neighbour without
having to undergo a tracheotomy. When the Tenants Selection Comm-
ittee heard my tale of harassment and intimidation, they wondered at the
cruelty of mankind and immediately allocated me a flat. From the moment I settled
in, life took an upward swing. Fanny no longer had to be smuggled in and out and I was no
longer tweeked and fondled. The flat was small but perfectly formed and I was surrounded by
chirpy neighbours.

One day, soon after I moved in, nothing happened. I waited all day and still noth-ing. And the next day was exactly the same. And the one after that, and the one after that. A pattern was beginning to emerge: If I sat in my chair all day without doing

anything, nothing would happen. It was quite clear that if I didn't put a stop to this inactivity soon I would turn into Samuel Beckett. I took my life by the scruff of the neck and gave it a good shake. What was this Gillian Pie Face nonsense? It wasn't me! I was a Fan Club and always had been. But what kind of Fan Club? Was it to be Carmen Miranda or Alfie Bass?*

*AT THIS POINT THE LOVELY PAUL MERTON AND I HAD A SERIOUS DISAGREEMENT. WHILE REFLECTING ON THE KIND OF FAN CLUB I WAS TO BECOME, WE BEGAN A HEATED DISCUSSION ABOUT THE NATURE OF CAMP AND THE ROLE OF CAMP HUMOUR IN THIS BOOK. I POINTED OUT THAT CAMP WAS IN MY BLOOD AND WOULD THEREFORE MANIFEST ITSELF AT EVERY OPPORTUNITY. PAUL WOULD SIMPLY HAVE TO PUT UP WITH IT. PAUL SAID HE HAD NO OBJECTIONS TO THE CAMP HUMOUR, PROVIDED IT WAS KEPT IN CHECK, AND THAT, IN PART, WAS WHAT HE CONSIDERED HIS ROLE AS CO-AUTHOR OF THIS BOOK TO BE. WITHOUT HIM THE WHOLE ENTERPRISE WOULD DEGENERATE INTO AN ENDLESS PARADE OF SAUCY INNUENDO AND MEN IN PICTURE HATS.
'QUEL DOMMAGE,' I SAID.
'WHAT DOES THAT MEAN?' SAID PAUL.

I ruminated all day on the variations available to the fertile imagination, but it wasn't until I was soaking in a hot bath that evening that I had a sudden flash of inspiration. *I shall call myself "The Joan Collins' Fan Club",'* I declared to the rubber duck.

At once I knew it was right. I'd long since been an admirer of that perennial actress.* *Dynasty* was at its peak and Joan smiled down from a thousand different magazine covers. As I stood dripping before the bathroom mirror my jaw dropped as another revelation hit me. I did, undeniably, bear an uncanny and unnatural resemblance to Joan Collins. The name was perfect and so was the profile! The whole act needed to go up market: the kaftan and the blond wig were wrong, glamour was what the cabaret circuit needed. As for Fanny, she was now ready to become a much more integral feature of the act. From now on she would be known as **FANNY THE WONDER DOG!** When I emerged from the bathroom that fateful day in a puff of Fenjal scented steam, I was a butterfly breaking away from the cocoon.

*HER TALENT IS AWESOME (IF YOU WANT AWE, SHE HAS SOME).

I fluttered about the living room,

liberated by the power of my own imagination.

The new strange persona that I had created

stretched its wings and flew towards the light.*

The cabaret circuit was beginning to expand and work was more plentiful. Some of the venues were small clubs in rooms above pubs and these were generally run on a profit share basis. However there were larger venues capable of holding several hundred punters and clearly large sums of money were to be made – though not by the performers.*

*A CAVERNOUS CLUB IN SOUTH LONDON CALLED LE RIP OFF WAS NOTORIOUS. CATERING TO THE WEALTHY YUPPIE MARKET, THEY WOULD CHARGE PUNTERS EIGHTY POUNDS A TICKET AND PAY THE ACTS A FIVER EACH.

The most infamous club in London was The Tunnel, run by Jeffrey Jabbawocky, a bulbous belching council tip in a suit. He once ate a live baby on stage to the tune of 'Ma, he's making eyes at me' but he could not go wrong as far as the regular audience was concerned. They were famous for their hostility towards the other acts. Abuse would be hurled on to the stage along with tables, chairs and whatever else was at hand. And when an act known to be unpopular was rebooked by Jeffrey, the audience would meet them at the railway station and dissuade them from performing by hanging them from a lamp-post. If, as a consequence, the evening was one act short, Jeffrey would keep the crowd happy by projecting colour slides of Parisian bridges on to his deformed genitalia.

Aware of the fearsome reputation these no-nonsense punters had, naturally I wondered how they would receive me now I was glamorised, clad in rubber and calling myself The Joan Collins' Fan Club. As a tape of Handel's Hallelujah thundered through the PA system, I made my grand entrance, scattering confetti over the front row before placing Fanny on a stool beside me. Already there were murmurings of discontent. We were seconds away from mayhem, but I thought I could perhaps tame them with vulgarity. But before I had time to say anything rude, the heckling began:

'Show us your bum!'

came a shout from the back. I immediately recognised the voice of Kingsley St Claire.

'Shut up and act like a man,' I retorted, *'or don't you do impressions?'* This got a laugh. Without waiting to be heckled further I turned to a man in the front row and asked him his name. It was Brian.

'What a lovely shirt you're wearing, Brian,' I said. *'Such a pity the shop didn't have your size. And now it's time to introduce you to Fanny the Wonder Dog.'* More applause, followed by 'oohs' and 'aahs' instead of 'grrrs'.

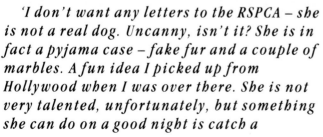

'I don't want any letters to the RSPCA – she is not a real dog. Uncanny, isn't it? She is in fact a pyjama case – fake fur and a couple of marbles. A fun idea I picked up from Hollywood when I was over there. She is not very talented, unfortunately, but something she can do on a good night is catch a

choc-drop. And I would like to hear thunderous applause if she manages to catch it. I don't know if you've got a spare hand, have you, Brian? But if you have, I would appreciate it if you'd put it together with the other one, to give Fanny and I the clap we so richly deserve.'

An expectant hush fell over the crowd, and as I threw the choc-drop into the air I realised for the first time the magnetic qualities of a bitch sitting on a stool with her mouth wide open.

She caught the choc-drop with nor

ant ease and at that moment she became a star. *

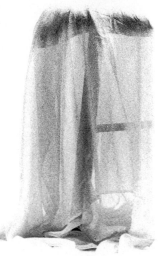

*FANNY: AT THAT MOMENT I BECAME A STAR, AND JULIAN BECAME A HANGER-ON. IT WAS OBVIOUS TO ME THAT THE CHOC-DROP ROUTINE WAS THE ONLY PART OF THE ACT THAT HAD ANY ARTISTIC MERIT. CLEARLY THE AUDIENCE WANTED MORE OF ME AND LESS OF HIM. HE WAS TOO CAMP AND THAT'S ALL THERE WAS TO IT. BUT I HAD TO STRETCH MYSELF IN OTHER AREAS. I DEVELOPED A TALENT FOR IMPRESSIONS: BY MOVING MY SNOUT SLOWLY FROM THE HORIZONTAL TO THE VERTICAL I COULD CREATE A PASSABLE LIKENESS OF TOWER BRIDGE. IF YOU CLOSED YOUR EYES YOU'D SWEAR YOU WERE IN DOCKLANDS. SOON MY REPERTOIRE EXPANDED TO INCLUDE SUCH NOTABLE LUMINARIES AS BETTE MIDLER, PETER DUNCAN AND MOTHER TERESA. THERE WERE UNPLEASANT SCENES BETWEEN JULIAN AND MYSELF AS MY ROLE WITHIN THE ACT INCREASED AND HIS DIMINISHED. HE WOULD SULK FOR DAYS EVERY TIME MY KATHARINE HEPBURN GOT A LAUGH. BUT THIS WAS THE TOUGH, COMPETITIVE WORLD OF SHOW BUSINESS AND YOU CAN'T AFFORD TO CARRY PASSENGERS IN THIS GAME. DEEP DOWN HE KNEW IT.

I was ready for the ultimate test – the
midnight show at the Comedy Store. By 'ultimate
test' I don't mean the twenty minutes on stage, I
mean the hours you had to spend in the dressing
room. Because the Comedy Store is situated in
Leicester Square, many comedians would drop
in after doing shows elsewhere in town. Thus
the small dressing rooms would bulge at the
seams, packed with the nation's up and coming
funny men and women. Peter Warren rarely
missed a Saturday night there. Usually he would
shuffle in looking despondent.

 'What's wrong, Peter?' someone would ask.
'Had a bad night?'

 'Yes, they just don't understand,' he would
say miserably. 'I was doing very well, then
somebody laughed!'

 People would murmur sympathetically. In the
midst of all these people and this jolly comic
banter, some of us would have to prepare
ourselves to go on stage. Each comedian has his
or her own personal ritual. For some this meant
a series of vocal exercises gleaned from some
friend of a friend at drama school. For Santini it
meant downing a bottle of brandy. But for me it
meant applying a great deal of make-up to my
face, and squeezing into skin-tight rubberwear.
Once this had been achieved the rubber had to
be given a shine with the aid of a can of Mr
Sheen and a duster. Parts of my anatomy were
beyond my reach and the assembled comedians
would squabble over who should have the
honour of polishing these nether regions. Some
people had firmer touches than others: I was
once left with 'Loadsa blisters' after being
over-polished by someone who shall remain
nameless.

One evening a young comedian by the name of Dave Dewfresh, who had only done two professional gigs, but had already been offered a summer season at the Johannesburg Palladium with Jimmy Tarbuck, discovered a hidden panel underneath the sink. Upon further investigation he found that the panel covered the entrance to a short passage, at the end of which was a large forgotten room. It was covered in cobwebs and filthy dirty, but fascinating nevertheless. He kept it a secret for quite some time, only going down to investigate when nobody else was around. Amazingly, this hidden room had been supplied with electricity, and once he had purchased the necessary light bulbs and screwed them into the appropriate sockets, he was able to see clearly for the first time just what he had discovered. The room was bare of furniture but around the walls hung a series of beautiful and breath-taking oil paintings – portraits of famous comedians. There were six in all. He studied each of them in turn, beginning with Dan Leno then moving on to Charlie Chaplin, Max Miller, Tony Hancock and Tommy Cooper. But intriguingly the final canvas was shrouded by a black velvet curtain. He stood silently before it for a few moments, then reached up and pulled the gold braided tassel that hung at the side. The curtains parted slowly and young Dave Dewfresh found himself staring incredulously at a newly painted portrait of himself.

Work that one out.

Fanny was having a hard time during this period. She was clearly a star and some of the other acts resented this. The Bicep Brothers were two knock-about-boys whose act consisted of making Lapsang Souchong tea and drinking it from bone china cups in a macho fashion. To find an elegant sensitive dog preening herself in the dressing room was more than they could stand so they hatched a plot to get rid of her once and for all. They persuaded their current girlfriends, who at this stage numbered one hundred and thirty-eight, to kidnap Fanny. Their planning was meticulous. One Friday, as chance would have it, Barry and Tony Bicep were on the same bill as me. As Tony lured me away from the dressing room with the offer of a tonic water and a close look at his comprehensive condom collection, Barry and the one hundred and thirty-eight women crept in and whisked Fanny away in a leatherette clutch bag. In an act of barbaric cruelty, that I can only describe as not nice, they took her to an environment that they knew would be anathema to her, or any sensitive living creature. They dumped her in Swansea. That would be the last anyone would hear of Fanny the Wonder Dog, so they thought. Of course they were wrong.*

*FANNY: AFTER SIXTEEN HOURS IN A LEATHERETTE CLUTCH BAG I WAS AMAZED TO DISCOVER MYSELF IN SWANSEA, BUT THEN I THOUGHT, WELL, YOU HAVE GOT TO DIE SOME TIME, SO YOU MIGHT AS WELL GET USED TO IT. I SET UP A COMPUTER DATING AGENCY WHICH WAS THRIVING BY THURSDAY AFTERNOON AND I HOPED THAT BY THE END OF THE WEEK I WOULD BE LADY MAYORESS – I WAS OBVIOUSLY BEST SUITED FOR THE JOB. IMAGINE MY SURPRISE WHEN IT WAS GIVEN TO SOMEBODY ELSE. I TOOK IMMEDIATE UMBRAGE AND CAUGHT THE NEXT TRAIN FOR LONDON. NOW I WAS MORE DETERMINED THAN EVER TO SUCCEED IN SHOW BUSINESS. IF THE BICEP BROTHERS WERE THAT WORRIED, I KNEW I HAD SOMETHING GOING FOR ME.

Upon Fanny's triumphant return I made a promise that I would never let her out of my sight again. The two of us sat down together and with meticulous precision planned the next stage of our joint career. The Edinburgh Fringe Festival was the shop window for new talent and we decided to put ourselves on display. Edinburgh during Festival time is a very peculiar place indeed. Rather than describe it myself, let me quote from a poem written by a medical student who trod the boards at the 1968 Festival in a hospital revue called *Bend Over Matron, I Want To Starch Your Pinny*. Here is his poem . . .

Oh Edinburgh, Edinburgh . . .

This poem captures perfectly not only the spirit but more importantly the spelling of that magnificent city.

Finding a suitable venue at an affordable price is, of course, no easy task. There are thousands of theatre groups competing for a limited number of spaces. Some unlucky people spent the entire three weeks performing up a tree. One such group was the London Transport Players who presented *Paint Your Wagon* up a willow in Princes Street Gardens. The audience perched on various branches and showed their appreciation by lobbing catkins at the orchestra. My first year was predictably a disaster. All I could afford was one square yard of cobblestone and I had to cancel the first week when somebody parked a Sierra Estate on top of it. It cost five thousand pounds a week and it wasn't even in Edinburgh. It was in Sunderland.

But back in London the cabaret circuit was spreading its tentacles far and wide. Work was plentiful, as were comedians. Talent and a compulsion to make people laugh were no longer vitally important factors. Careers teachers would advise students to forget about merchant banking and instead concentrate on getting an open spot at the Comedy Store. Any child that so much as doodled in the margin of his/her exercise book was immediately presumed to be a comic genius. Instead of being groomed for grammar school he/she was heavily encouraged to do impressions of David Coleman.

I was now getting as much work as I could handle and Fanny's popularity was giving me cause for some chagrin. Her impressions and her choc-drop routine were much-loved and during her enforced visit to Swansea I was harangued by cries of *'Where's the dog?'* I realised I was in danger of becoming a straight man and we certainly didn't want that. I needed to re-assert myself by devising some comic business whereby I was undeniably the star and Fanny a mere extra. I was pondering upon this one night and idly watching *Dynasty* when the idea hit me like a thunder bolt. Expanding on my ability to humiliate members of the public with my waspish tongue, I would take the ritual one stage further. I would write my own *Dynasty* script wherein I would play the part of Alexis and some unfortunate supply teacher type from the audience would be Blake. I quickly wrote the script, a sordid selection of smutty innuendo and very old jokes.

If memory serves me correctly it went something like this:

Alexis: *Good morning, Blake, I trust you slept well?*

Blake: *Yes thank you, like a log; I woke up in the fireplace. I saw you on the telly last night.*

Alexis: *I'll sleep anywhere when I'm drunk.*

Blake: *Has the milkman come yet?*

Alexis: *No, but he is breathing heavily.*

Blake: *By God, Alexis, when I was a milkman I never left an empty behind.*

Alexis: *Was that your daughter I heard screaming?*

Blake: *Yes, she makes a lot of noise but her heart is in the right place.*

Alexis: *Pity about the rest of her. I'm sorry to hear that Krystle gave birth to six piglets in the night.*

Blake: *Yes and I want to know the swine responsible.*

Alexis: *What nice trousers you're wearing, Blake.*

Blake: *Yes, Krystle made them for me.*

Alexis: *Perhaps she should use a pattern in future. There's no need to take them off, Blake. They're not that bad.*

Blake: *But I insist, you're driving me wild with desire.*

Alexis: *Get a grip on yourself, Blake!*

Blake: *Do you remember the first words I spoke to you?*

Alexis: *No, I don't.*

Blake: *My name's Blake Carrington, but you can call me Big-knob.*

Alexis: *And then you offered me a job as your secretary.*

Blake: *I needed someone to help me with my enormous mail.*

Alexis: *It was nothing I couldn't handle.*

Blake: *I can't go on, Alexis. I'm a wreck, a ruin and a shrine to despair. Leave me! Leave me! There's only one thing that will make me feel better now and that's to sing that old Roger Whittaker classic, 'I'm Gonna Leave Old Durham Town' at the top of my voice . . .*

(Sings):

I'm gonna leave old Durham Town,
I'm gonna leave old Durham Town,
I'm gonna leave old Durham Town,
and that leaving's gonna get me down.

This part of the act swiftly became a favourite of audiences everywhere, with the exception of Kim Wells who said it was *'crap'*. The success of it depended on picking the right punter from the audience. Sadly, this was a lesson I took some time to learn. My mistakes were many and varied. I've dealt with them all in my time, I can tell you. I remember one particular occasion at Trent Poly in Nottingham where a punter called Keith dropped his trousers and knocked somebody's hat off in the front row. He was so drunk and out of order he not only belched his way through the script but when it came to the song he refused to sing 'Old Durham Town' and instead launched into three choruses of 'She Was Only The Engine Driver's Daughter But She Ran Off With A Puff'. I soon learnt how to avoid men like him; splashes of vomit on the shoes were a sure sign that I should steer clear.

CHAPTER NINE

HANDLE ME GENTLY, MR WATERCRESS!

'PEOPLE TREAT YOU THE WAY YOU TREAT YOURSELF.' SONDRA RAY, 'LOVING RELATIONSHIPS'.

It was around this time, dear reader, that I received another visit from Ernie Moss. I was standing at the sink, rinsing out my doilies, when I heard a familiar cry from the living room.

'Aye, aye, not many in tonight. I came home the other day and I said to the wife, "Ere, I've just heard that the milkman has made love to every woman in this street, bar one," and she said, "I bet it's that stuck-up cow at number thirty-four."'

I was pleasantly surprised to see him. All his previous visits had been to the tiny attic room that I'd rented off Mr Bishop. *'I wondered where you got to,'* I said.

'Oh knocking about, ducking and diving,' he replied, giving Fanny a gentle pat on the head. *'Well, you've moved up in the world since the last time I saw you,'* he said as he wafted around the room toying with my bibelots.*

'I'm very pleased for you.'
'Thank you,' I said.

'But, and it's a big but,' he warned.
'How big?' I said.

'One of the biggest buts you're ever likely to come across,' he said seriously.

'Well, I once had a very large maybe and that was quite enough for me.'

'I'm not talking maybe, I'm not talking perhaps. I'm talking buts. Not ifs, but buts.'

'But buts?' I said. *'You sound like a motor boat.'*

'I am a motor boat,' he said gravely. *'And I'd like to take you for a bob round the bay.'*

'But about your but,' I said, trying to keep my grasp on some kind of reality.

*KNICK KNACKS. I HAD QUITE AN IMPRESSIVE COLLECTION INCLUDING A QUEEN ANNE SNUFF BOX; THE VERY BOX IN WHICH QUEEN ANNE SNUFFED IT.

'My but is but a short distance into the future, which is where we are going now,' he said. Before I could ask him what he meant a sudden burst of brilliant white light caused me to cover my eyes. A floating sensation overcame me, I reached out towards the mantelpiece but it wasn't there. The cry of a seagull over head startled me into opening my eyes. I found myself aboard a small motor boat rocking on a clear blue sea. The sun was shining down, Ernie Moss was at the helm and Fanny was sunning herself on a plateau of red chenille cushions.

'Oh Ernie,' I said, overcome with emotion. 'I . . . I . . . I . . . think I'm going to cry.'

'Now then,' said Ernie, giving me a stern look. 'I haven't brought you here to have a good sob. There's lessons to be learned. Now I mentioned a but and it's not far away now. It's getting nearer all the time. In fact it's nearer now than when I started this sentence. Here goes. You've been doing quite well at the old comedy lark for the past few months. You've changed your name, you've changed your image, you're getting laughs, the dog's getting laughs. But you need management, you need handling.' I nodded enthusiastically. 'You've got to be moulded as soon as possible. Otherwise you will go round that cabaret circuit for years, lapping the newcomers as they join the race. That's where I went wrong. Forty years I played the halls up and down the country living out of a suitcase. Mind you it was a big suitcase. Had to be, what with the wife and the whippets. I came home one night, saw the wife crying her eyes out. I said, "What's the matter with you?" She said, "I'm home sick." I said, "This is your home," and she said, "I know and I am sick of it," and that's not what I want for you.'

'It's not what I want for myself,' I said.

'Well, you take a tip from old Ernie Moss,' he said, winking at me. 'He'll see you right.'

'Thank you, Ernie,' I said, giving him a friendly wink back.

In the fraction of a second that my eyelid was closed, the idyllic scene transformed itself. As my eye opened up from the wink I found myself back in my flat with Fanny at my side and no sign of the boat, the sea or Ernie. Just a gentle wisp of smoke about the mantelpiece. *'Management,'* I pondered, still feeling the warm tingle of the sun on my forehead. Surely they couldn't all be as unsavoury as Kingsley St Claire?

Naïvety was my middle name. The first twelve potential managers all wanted to see my bum before they would consider me. I thought I'd struck it lucky with number thirteen. Our telephone conversation was promising enough. An appointment was made for three o'clock the following Tuesday, so at three o'clock the following Tuesday I found myself outside the door of Mr Ginger Willis, manager to the stars. I knocked.

'Come in,' a voice purred. I entered a plush office. The smell of leather and cigars stung my nostrils. A stubby hand reached out from behind a vast mahogany desk.

'I hope you like my office,' said Ginger Willis in tones reminiscent of Fenella Fielding. *'It's very plush, isn't it?'*

'Very,' I agreed, already unsure if I wanted this man to handle my future, let alone anything else. I looked around at the dozens of photographs that covered every inch of available wall space. And as he got up to pour a drink I saw that he even had a picture pinned to his back. *'Are all these your clients?'* I asked. *'Oh no,'* he said, handing me a whisky that I hadn't asked for. *'No, they're just the celebrities who have offered me the sexual services of their children in return for a summer season in Scarborough with Vince Hill. Interested?'* he asked, arching an eyebrow with a perfect curve. *'Not my bag, Ginge,'* I said, realising that perhaps I had made a dreadful mistake by coming to see this orange ogre.

'Quite,' he snapped. *'Trick question. Cigar?'* He pushed towards me a brown cylindrical object that I can only describe as a cheroot. I shook my head. *'I am a busy man,'* he breathed, *'so I'll come straight to the point. You have a big future ahead of you. But the man in the street will never accept a boy in black rubber. It's too kinky. So what I want to say to you is quite simple: stiletto heels, petticoats and plastic tits.'* I winced. *'Why the wince?'* he said, both eyebrows joining forces to create a perfect rhomboid.

'I'm not, nor will I ever be, a drag act,' I said firmly.

'Then you will never work in Scarborough,' he said.

There seemed little point in continuing the interview. If I was to fulfil Ernie Moss' vision I would have to look elsewhere. Later that evening over a cup of warm Horlicks and a box of chocolate brazils I perused my list of potential managers.

Everybody on the list had been tried, apart from one. Flaxton Watercress. I hadn't thought him worth considering before, mainly because he had a stupid name. He was a fifteen-year-old spotty adolescent who'd been bunking off school since the age of five. He had made his first thousand from a bit of this and that; he would buy 'this' for next to nothing and sell 'that' at a huge profit. His involvement with cabaret stemmed from the early days at the Tunnel. Having seen the audience throw chairs at the acts it didn't like, his sharp business mind saw a chance to make money. There were never enough chairs to go round, so he soon set up a stall in the car park, selling battered chairs and occasional tables.

'Roll up! Roll up!' he'd shout. *'If you wanna chuck a chair, chuck one of these.'*

With the money from this venture he set himself up as a promoter and manager. He had found me occasional work, usually in seedy polytechnics, but apart from that we'd had few dealings with each other. The idea of placing my future in the hands of someone still wearing short trousers seemed ridiculous, but I had tried all the others without success.

So I took a deep breath and rang Flaxton Watercress.

He wasn't there. According to the garbled message

on his answerphone he had been given detention for making

stupid noises during metal work so he wouldn't be back till half-past six. I left a message

saying I was seeking management, and he rang back at seven o'clock to say that he had already arranged

a three-week tour of North West England, nineteen regional radio interviews, a record deal with an option on a video album and a series for London Weekend Television.

'Probably,' he added.

'So you're my manager, then?' I asked.

'Yes, mush,' he replied. 'Come round and see me tomorrow night. And bring me a packet of fags, will you? They won't sell them to me round here.'

The meeting was a success and it was agreed that Flaxton should represent me from now on. 'Got to get you on the telly, my son,' he said, which struck me as odd considering how much younger than me he was. 'And another thing, mush, I want you off that cabaret circuit, you're cheapening yourself. Get an hour's worth of material together and we're off on tour.' The similarity between these words and the advice of Ernie Moss struck me at once. It was uncanny, not to say unnatural. I was put into such a tizz by his plans that it wasn't until the next day that I realised Flaxton had sold me three chairs and a coffee table.

One morning Flaxton phoned me in a more excitable state than usual. The words came tumbling out of the ear-piece in such a mish-mash that it was some minutes before I realised I was listening to Flaxton and not some lunatic talking too quickly. 'I got you some telly, mush,' he conveyed to me at last. 'This Wednesday, ten o'clock, live from the Royal Albert Hall. Must dash, see you there at nine,' and with that he put the phone down. He hadn't told me what to wear or what material to use, or even how long my slot was.

He was strangely unavailable over the intervening days and it wasn't until I met him at the appointed time and place that the awful truth became apparent. It was indeed live television from the Royal Albert Hall, but not quite the type of programme we had imagined. Fanny the Wonder Dog was to fight Joe Bugner over fifteen rounds, and I was to mop Fanny's brow in between each and every one of those rounds. I protested somewhat, but he shoved a bucket and a J-cloth into my hand before

disappearing round the front of the Albert Hall where he had a stall selling chairs and souvenir biscuit tins.

It seemed unfair to put Fanny into the ring with Joe Bugner, but what could I do? There were over four thousand punters baying for blood out there, and, although I knew it was cruelty to dumb animals, I let the fight go ahead. Mercifully Fanny knocked Joe out in the third round and put an end to his suffering. However, I wouldn't call the evening a total success since the opportunities for getting my comic lines across to the television viewers were next to none. As Joe lay spread-eagled on the canvas, I did manage a quick 'Who cuts your hair for you – is it the council?' before the referee waved me away. Call me over-sensitive, dear reader, but I don't think the boxing fraternity is quite ready for camp humour. Mind you, I did once see Harry Carpenter in a puff-ball skirt, but I think he was raising money for charity.*

*AT LEAST THAT'S WHAT HE TOLD THE POLICE.

Flaxton scurried into the dressing room afterwards to congratulate Fanny and I. He introduced me to his girlfriend Monica. Theirs was a serious relationship and had been for several minutes. He said he truly loved her and such sincerity touched me.*

Fanny's victory over Joe Bugner gave her delusions of grandeur. She refused to go anywhere by public transport and our taxi bills were enormous. I was furious with Flaxton and told him in no uncertain terms that unless he found me another, and more suitable, TV appearance immediately, I would seek management elsewhere.

*UNTIL I REALISED IT WAS THE REFEREE LOOKING FOR HIS DICKIE-BOW.

'I've got a big one in the pipeline'

'No, no, no, mush,' said a worried Flaxton,

'Then phone Dyno-rod,' I snapped, aware that I had made a joke that wasn't a sexual innuendo for the first time in my life.

'Calm down, calm down, it's a mad house here. Everything is under control, mush.' He jibbered on like this for several minutes until I was compelled to hang up. Knowing the rate at which he worked, I figured he would have something sorted out by half-past two that afternoon. At two-thirty exactly the phone rang.

'Saturday Night Live,' said Flaxton. *'Sorted. Seven minutes. Next Saturday. How does that grab you?'*

'Never you mind,' I said, secretly thrilled to the marrow. I had seen the programme before, but it wasn't until I arrived at the studio that I realised quite how frightening it all was. The studio was the size of Heathrow Airport, with a little bit of Luton for your dressing room. I was to perform on Stage C beneath a giant inflatable balaclava, while seven or eight cameras jostled for my attention.* As the name suggests, *Saturday Night Live* was broadcast live on Saturday nights, and as the seconds ticked by I felt several beads of sweat on my forehead, which I quickly fashioned into a necklace. Terror gripped me by the throat and fear had a quick rummage in my drawers. I tried to relax on the small velour divan in my dressing room, but there was no escaping the fact that in a matter of minutes I would be appearing on millions of television sets throughout the country. As I shakily powdered my nose one last time, I fancied I saw, reflected in the mirror, the ghostly image of Ernie Moss. He gave me a nod and a wink, and this reminder of his omnipotent presence was enough to galvanise my quivering soul. I passed through the terror barrier, and as I minced on to Stage C that evening I felt a serenity that is normally only associated with royalty.**

*I ONLY HAD EYES FOR CAMERA 2.

**AND WE ALL KNOW WHAT THEY'RE ON.

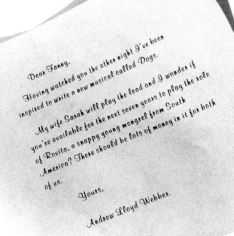

Dear Fanny,

Having watched you the other night I've been inspired to write a new musical called Dogs.

My wife Sarah will play the lead and I wonder if you're available for the next seven years to play the role of Rovita, a snappy young mongrel from South America? There should be lots of money in it for both of us.

Yours,

Andrew Lloyd Webber.

Her Royal Highness Fanny the Wonder Dog had never been in better form. She obviously realised the importance of these few short minutes on the small screen. She gazed soulfully into the cameras and instantly captured the hearts of the nation. Many of them have felt compelled to write to her.

Fanny, I need you. Your glistening coat has stoked up a fire within my loins. I haven't felt this way since Susan Hampshire got me at it in The Forsyte Saga. Say when and where.

Signed, A Dog Lover.

Flaxton wasted no time in organising a nationwide tour. Thirty dates were pencilled in and it was now imperative that I came up with an hour's worth of material. It was while I was pondering this one day and tucking into a nice juicy nectarine that I felt a song in my heart and a yodel in my throat. I wasn't at all musical but, what the heck, neither were Bananarama. People laughed at their singing so why shouldn't they laugh at mine? I immediately put the word out on the circuit that I needed a pianist. Several names were put forward so I arranged an audition.

First up to the keyboards was Nelly Clackett, a foul-mouthed washer
woman from Peckham who might have got the job if she hadn't used
my clutch-bag as a spitoon. Next came Wallis Cake, ex-army corporal,
whose idea of a good time was a naked woman. I tried out a few jokes
about private parts and standing to attention, but didn't raise so much

as a smile. I knew we would never hit
it off. Several other applicants of various
shapes and sizes were given their chance.
Some were musically inept, others socially
inadequate, e.g. corduroy trousers. The final
hopeful was a young whippersnapper who'd
snapped many a whip in his time. He played
the piano with grace until I told Grace to
shove-off and let him play it on his own. His
name was Russell and having heard him play
most beautifully, I thought, perhaps, I had
found my accompanist. He was young, fresh-
faced and didn't care who knew it.

*'You're very young and fresh-faced, aren't
you?'* I said.

'Yes, and I don't care who knows it,' he
replied with more than a touch of arrogant
puppy about him. I perused his CV for the first
time and my eyes fell upon a dirty and
unacceptable word – Cambridge. I shuddered
visibly.

'*You're shuddering visibly,*' he observed.

'*There is little point in shuddering invisibly,*' I snapped. '*I'm not ashamed of my shudders. When I shudder I want the whole world to know about it.*'

'*When I was at Cambridge,*' he said in a bragging tone, '*people who shuddered were considered riff-raff.*'

'*Don't ever say that word again!*' I shouted, giving him a sharp slap to the back of the leg.

'*What word?*' he said, bewildered, and beginning a shudder all of his own.

'*The C-word,*' I said.

'*Oh,* that *word, whyever not? Shall we talk about Proust instead?*'

I took a deep breath. '*I think you're a nice boy Russell, and a brilliant pianist, but if you're going to work with me we must first scrape off the slime and scum that has accrued in three years at Cambridge University.*'

'*But my friends at the BBC—*' he began.

'*Are no friends of mine,*' I interjected, perhaps overstating things in my efforts to make myself plain. '*And another thing,*' I said, feeling my emotions building to a crescendo, '*I very much suspect you of being a heterosexual. If this is so, then I presume you cannot help yourself. But I implore you, tell me now, once and for all, which side of the church are you accustomed to sitting on?*'

'*I stand at the back,*' he stammered, hedging his bets.

'*That's not good enough!*' I thundered.*

'*All right,*' he blurted out, falling to his knees. '*I like women.*'

'*Just as I thought,*' I said, helping him to his feet. '*Well thank you for coming to the audition, we'll let you know.*' I smiled weakly as I jotted the words 'Cambridge heterosexual' at the top of his CV, already reconsidering Wallis Cake. As he slouched towards the exit, Fanny, who had been silent till now, suddenly jumped off her cushion and scampered after young Russell. He stopped in the doorway and Fanny leapt into his arms, smothering his face with doggy kisses. As I observed this poignant scene I saw that the decision had been taken out of my hands, and Russell at that moment became the pianist of The Joan Collins' Fan Club.

*THUNDERING IS UNUSUAL FOR ME. BUT A MAN GROWS TIRED OF SHUDDERING AND A JOLLY GOOD THUNDERING CAN CLEAR THE TUBES.

I swiftly rechristened him the 'Lovely Russell With His Gorgeous Upright'. The former being mere satire and the latter being a reference to his instrument. He had a tough task ahead of him. On the first day of rehearsal I said, *'Russell give me a B flat – on second thoughts just give me a B and I will flatten it myself.'*

I hadn't sung publicly since the days of the 'Get 'Em Off' Singing Telegram Agency, and I was understandably nervous. There was a considerable difference between a quick 'Happy Birthday, Dear Janice' in a crowded saloon bar, and warbling to the paying public on a national tour. The lovely Russell's face darkened with worry as he said for the umpteenth time, *'Let's try that once again, shall we?'* and that was only clearing my throat. But with a grim dedication on my part and expert tuition from 'The Boy' we soon discovered that I didn't have a note in my head. This was of no concern to me. If the public wanted to hear proper singing they could go and see John Hanson in *The Student Prince*. I offered much more than mere singing – people didn't buy tickets to see my epiglottis; instead they wanted to catch a ride on the hem of my chiffon cape to a world of waspish glamour and eternal double entendre. As emperor of this land and driver of the chariot, I could do more or less as I pleased. My rendition of such classic songs as 'Get The Meat Balls Out, Mother, We Are Coming To A Fork In The Road'* was unique, and songs written by the lovely Russell and myself were equally well received. Who can forget that country and western favourite 'You Put Sugar In My Tea Again, You Bastard'?:

Bone structure strong, moral fibre weak,
General outlook wrong, long-range forecast bleak.
I thought that love was up for grabs,
But all you gave to me was crabs,
You're the disappointment of my week,
I'm now covered in ointment and I reek.
You put sugar in my tea again, you bastard!

*SOMETIMES SUBSTITUTED FOR 'I USED TO KISS HIM ON THE LIPS, BUT IT'S ALL OVER NOW' OR EVEN 'GET OFF THE STOVE GRANDMA, YOU'RE TOO OLD TO RIDE THE RANGE'.

During these musical interludes Fanny would recline on a cushion at the side of the stage, exuding star quality. Occasionally an over-enthusiastic punter would rush the stage and attempt to stroke her. This would start a trend, and before you knew it dozens of adoring fans would be running down the aisles, their arms out-stretched towards Fanny, hoping to pluck a souvenir tuft of fur. When bald patches appeared on her back I thought it prudent to employ a body guard. This came in the shape of Grazio – six foot of rippling Maltese muscle. No one ever laid a finger on Fanny again. She became untouchable.

Russell's role within the act took the form of a whipping post. He didn't open his mouth much but whatever he did say was wrong. I saw to that.

'What do you want to do when you grow up, Russell?'

  'I want to have your babies, Julian.'

'I make him say that.'

  Things were moving very quickly now. Fanny was in great demand and somehow I managed to tag along. She became the focus of intense media attention: radio, television, newspapers – all came knocking at my door. Researchers and reporters popped out from the most unexpected places, asking the most predictable questions.

Q: Where do you get your ideas from?
A: From wherever ideas come from.

Q: Why The Joan Collins' Fan Club?
A: It came to me in a dream.

Q: Who thought of the act.
  Was it you or Fanny?
A: I did. Fanny's just a dog.

  It all became a bit of a strain. Sometimes I put lipstick on Grazio and let him do the interview. Fanny and I were achieving the success that we had worked for over the years. And while this was gratifying there were some aspects of the process that were difficult to cope with. When you are constantly flattered by the attentions of devoted fans, who see you as some kind of guru, and you read in the newspapers that apparently you are talented and exciting, the ego, despite itself, is handed a distorted view of reality. Badly behaved Hollywood actors and immature pop stars who smash up hotel rooms and make excessive demands on the people around them have been engulfed by an ego overstuffed on a diet of pure hype. I was surrounded by hype, and my self-esteem was as voracious

as the next man's. As indeed was Fanny's. She became a primadonna trapped in a dog's body. Strutting into hotel suites, she would howl at the slightest aesthetic indiscretion. At the Adelphi Hotel, Liverpool, we had to change rooms three times until she was satisfied that her bed-spread was a suitable match for the curtains. And Russell's dress sense was a constant irritation to her. Nevertheless the tour was a great success. After thirty dates in as many days we returned to London, triumphant but exhausted.

There was a surprise waiting for me when I returned. During my absence, Flaxton had taken it upon himself to have my humble flat completely re-decorated. Gone was the simple but functional furniture that I had collected about me over the years, and gone were the simple white walls. My home was unrecognisable. My manager considered it unseemly that a person in my position should live like an ordinary mortal. He had once read in a magazine that Elizabeth Taylor insisted on lilac walls, lilac carpets and lilac furnishings in any environment in which she was to spend more than twelve seconds.* Flaxton felt what was good enough for Elizabeth Taylor was good enough for me.

DO remember that I am the star of the show. The public come to see me and not you. Without me you'd be a nobody, like Russell.

DON'T expect me to be around much anymore. I am now part of the International Jet Set. For example, this evening, I shall be dining out with Susannah York at the Savoy, so you can stick your Winalot up your arse.

DO stay out of the way if I bring Susannah back for coffee.

DON'T hang around the kitchen waiting to be introduced to her. She doesn't know who you are, and she doesn't care.

But quite why he chose maroon to decorate my flat I shall never know. When I first saw it I smiled at Flaxton weakly, trying to hide my true feelings – but Fanny was more straight-forward; she was sick on the carpet. (She'd been eating beetroot, so it took me five days to find it.) In fact Fanny was becoming increasingly sophisticated in her tastes – and less tolerant. One morning I was amazed to find a list of 'Do's and Don'ts' on the maroon kitchen table:

*A MAN CALLED TONY WEBSTER IS EMPLOYED TO WALK TEN YARDS IN FRONT OF ELIZABETH TAYLOR, PAINTING EVERYTHING WITH LILAC EMULSION. UNEXPECTED DETOURS ON THE PART OF ELIZABETH COULD LEAD TO ALL KINDS OF COMPLICATIONS; NOT ONLY MIGHT SHE FIND HERSELF IN MAGNOLIA SURROUNDINGS, TONY MIGHT BE OFF SOMEWHERE ELSE, NEEDLESSLY PAINTING FIVE CHAIRS AND A TALL BOY.

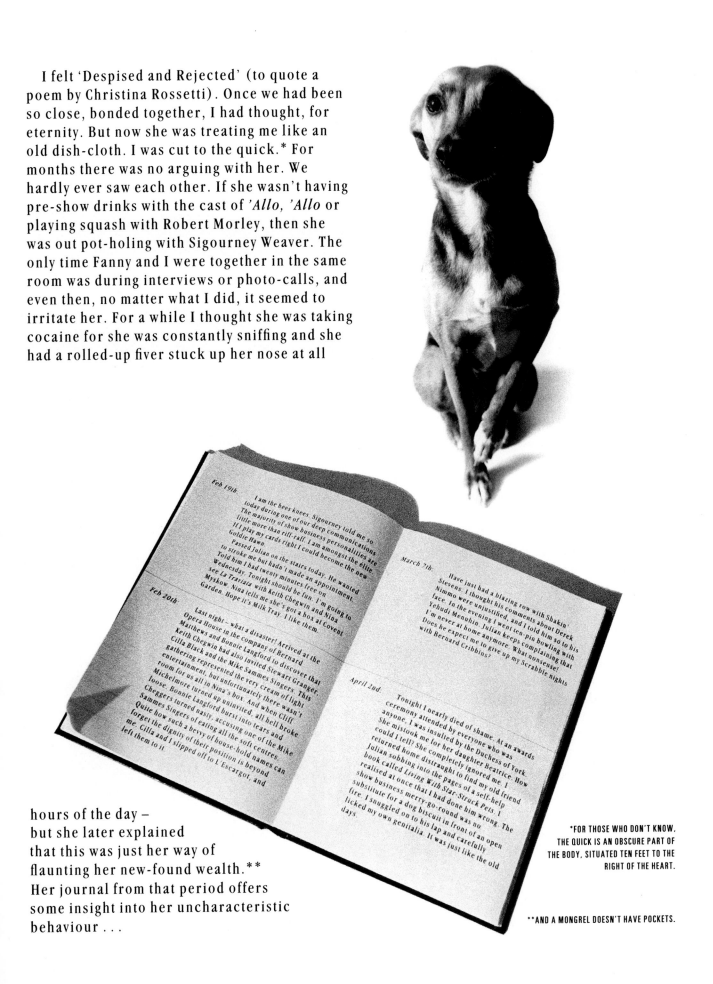

I felt 'Despised and Rejected' (to quote a poem by Christina Rossetti). Once we had been so close, bonded together, I had thought, for eternity. But now she was treating me like an old dish-cloth. I was cut to the quick.* For months there was no arguing with her. We hardly ever saw each other. If she wasn't having pre-show drinks with the cast of *'Allo, 'Allo* or playing squash with Robert Morley, then she was out pot-holing with Sigourney Weaver. The only time Fanny and I were together in the same room was during interviews or photo-calls, and even then, no matter what I did, it seemed to irritate her. For a while I thought she was taking cocaine for she was constantly sniffing and she had a rolled-up fiver stuck up her nose at all

Feb 19th:
I am the bees knees. Sigourney told me so today during one of our deep communications. The majority of show business personalities are little more than riff-raff. I am amongst the élite. If I play my cards right I could become the new Goldie Hawn. Passed Julian on the stairs today. He wanted to stroke me but hadn't made an appointment. Told him I had twenty minutes free on Wednesday. Tonight should be fun. I'm going to see *La Traviata* with Keith Chegwin and Nina Myskow. Nina tells me she's got a box at Covent Garden. Hope it's Milk Tray. I like them.

Feb 20th:
Last night – what a disaster! Arrived at the Opera House in the company of Bernard Matthews and Bonnie Langford to discover that Keith Chegwin had also invited Stewart Granger. Cilla Black and the Mike Sammes Singers. This gathering represented the very cream of light entertainment, but unfortunately there wasn't room for us all in Nina's box. And when Cliff Michelmore turned up uninvited, all hell broke loose. Bonnie Langford burst into tears and Cheggers turned nasty, accusing one of the Mike Sammes Singers of eating all the soft centres. Quite how such a bevy of house-hold names can forget the dignity of their position is beyond me. Cilla and I slipped off to L'Escargot, and left them to it.

March 7th:
Have just had a blazing row with Shakin' Stevens. I thought his comments about Derek Nimmo were unjustified, and I told him so to his face. In the evening I went ten-pin bowling with Yehudi Menuhin. Julian keeps complaining that I'm never at home anymore. What nonsense! Does he expect me to give up my Scrabble nights with Bernard Cribbins?

April 2nd:
Tonight I nearly died of shame. At an awards ceremony attended by everyone who was anyone, I was insulted by the Duchess of York. She mistook me for her daughter Beatrice. How could I tell? She completely ignored me. I returned home distraught to find my old friend Julian sobbing into the pages of a self-help book called *Living With Star-Struck Pets.* I realised at once that I had done him wrong. The show business merry-go-round was no substitute for a dog biscuit in front of an open fire. I snuggled on to his lap and carefully licked my own genitalia. It was just like the old days.

hours of the day –
but she later explained
that this was just her way of
flaunting her new-found wealth.**
Her journal from that period offers
some insight into her uncharacteristic
behaviour . . .

*FOR THOSE WHO DON'T KNOW, THE QUICK IS AN OBSCURE PART OF THE BODY, SITUATED TEN FEET TO THE RIGHT OF THE HEART.

**AND A MONGREL DOESN'T HAVE POCKETS.

CHAPTER TEN

DIRTY BUSINESS

'FOR MAN IS MAN AND MASTER OF HIS FATE'.
ALFRED LORD TENNYSON.

To catch up on the latest gossip I decided to pay a visit to the Comedy Store. Many of my old friends were there – Santini, Jeffrey Jabbawocky and Peter Warren to name but three.

'How are you?' Jeffrey asked as I walked into the dressing room.

'Very well, thanks,' I said cheerfully.

'Well, you don't look it,' said Jeffrey, pushing past me. Peter Warren was similarly offhand and only a sozzled Santini offered me a friendly slurp from his brandy bottle. Some people clearly regarded my success as a kind of treachery. Access to their friendship was conditional upon me earning no more than thirty-five pounds per night. And while I chatted to those who were pleased to see me, others stood murmuring in the shadows, as if my current popularity was in some way a barrier to their own progress. Well, that's show biz. Take it or leave it.

However, there was a lighter side to my visit that evening. A punter came up to me and identified himself as a member of The Fan Club Unfortunates. This self-help support group consisted of all the traumatised members of the public who had played Blake on stage in the aforementioned *Dynasty* script. Meetings were held nationwide. Men who were now figures of fun gathered together to exorcise ghostly memories of public humiliation. Together they hoped to claw their way back to a dignified position in society. The group had been founded two years before by a man called Chuck.

Chuck had been enjoying the evening's cabaret at Le Rip Off with a large party of friends when his gingham shirt had caught my eye. And when he told me his name I knew I was on to a winner.

'Chuck as in heave?' I asked and got a huge laugh.

From that moment on Chuck had been referred to as Heave by all his pals. The nickname drove him to the brink of insanity, until he happened to meet another unfortunate 'Blake' in a pub. Together they saved each other from complete mental disintegration. Thereafter they advertised in under-ground magazines and were now so organised they leafleted the audiences leaving my gigs, offering them immediate counselling. I asked the punter if he had one such leaflet about his person and he swiftly produced one.

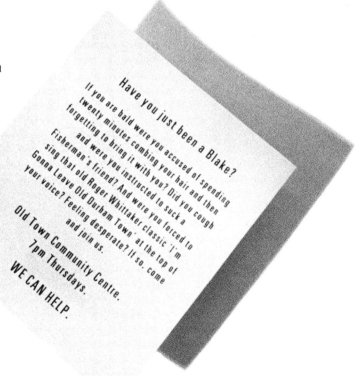

Have you just been a Blake?

If you are bald were you accused of spending twenty minutes combing your hair and then forgetting to bring it with you? Did you cough and were you instructed to suck a Fisherman's friend? And were you forced to sing that old Roger Whittaker classic 'I'm Gonna Leave Old Durham Town' at the top of your voice? Feeling desperate? If so, come and join us.

Old Town Community Centre.
7pm Thursdays.

WE CAN HELP.

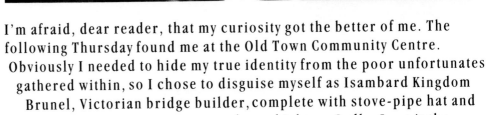

I'm afraid, dear reader, that my curiosity got the better of me. The following Thursday found me at the Old Town Community Centre. Obviously I needed to hide my true identity from the poor unfortunates gathered within, so I chose to disguise myself as Isambard Kingdom Brunel, Victorian bridge builder, complete with stove-pipe hat and mutton-chop whiskers. Sadly, I got it the wrong way round and I entered the hall with stove-pipe whiskers and a mutton-chop hat.

Inside the hall were gathered thirty or forty men of every shape and size with one thing in common, the look of a tortured squirrel that hadn't seen his nuts for a fortnight. I tried to emulate this look myself lest my true identity be discovered, but the best I could manage was the look of a water vole who had just glimpsed a council employee relieving himself upstream.* I took a seat at the back and waited for the fun to begin. Hopefully there would be scenes of despair and mass hysteria. The lights dimmed and the men round me began a low chant.

Men like us don't grow in trees.

Usually we swing from them.

This mantra was repeated ad nauseam for what seemed like hours, until the spell was broken by a man I immediately recognised as Chuck, or should I say Heave? *'Gentlemen,'* he began gravely. *'We have all been victims of audience participation. Is there one amongst us who hasn't had his hair cut by the council?'* A man next to me began to sob. The scene began to affect me very deeply, not because I had an ounce of sympathy for these poor wretches but because I had never heard my lines delivered so badly before.

I was about to rip side-burns and hat from my head and confront these imbeciles with their own stupidity, when I saw to my horror that the lovely Russell was sitting in the front row. Just at that moment he sprang to his feet and began to testify, asking 'brother Chuck' to cast this devilish camp from his infected mind and replace it with the old Liverpudlian cod that he was once loved for. At this, he fell jibbering to the floor, speaking, as it would seem, in many tongues. I managed to decipher the odd *'Release me!'* It was a pathetic sight and I couldn't help but feel sorry for him.

Quite clearly I had underestimated the cumulative effect of my on-stage treatment of him.* Having to say out loud *'I am a nobody',* and then *'Julian, I think you are wonderful'* every night, was not good for his personal sense of worth, but being chastised for his heterosexuality into the bargain had tipped the scales. The sensitive soul of a talented musician was being slowly trampled on by my stage persona's need for superiority, achieved by any means. And that's just the way I like it.

I shuffled surreptitiously towards the doorway. I paused for one last look at the poor pathetic wretches whose lives had been irrevocably shattered for the sake of a cheap laugh.

*OFF STAGE I TREATED HIM LIKE DIRT, BUT SO WHAT? HE GETS PAID. ANYWAY, I THINK HE QUITE LIKES IT.

I toyed with the idea of whipping off my hat and whiskers and shouting, *'Cooee, boys, I'm over here!'*, but at the sound of a throbbing taxi outside in the street, I made my exit.

'Where to?' said the cheerful cockney cabbie.

'Anywhere,' I said.**

**HE TOOK ME TO A PART OF ANYWHERE THAT I HAD NEVER SEEN BEFORE. IT WAS SO BORING IT COULD HAVE BEEN CHESTER.

CHAPTER ELEVEN

A WOOF IN THE PARK

'LIFE IS A FULL-TIME OCCUPATION.' JEANETTE THERESE OBSTOJ.

One morning I got a phone call from Flaxton.

'Pack your bags, mush – I've fixed up another nationwide tour.'

'Another one?'

'You're hot cakes at the moment. I've got you thirty dates in twelve days: Glasgow, Portsmouth, Aberdeen, Cardiff, Lowestoft, and that's just Wednesday. The tour finishes at the Hackney Empire.' I told him that Fanny and I were too tired, but he said the T-shirts were already printed.

That evening I wearily packed my Louis Vuitton suitcase with twelve days' supply of dog food. As I chewed on a vitamin pill I doubted for a moment my own capacity to cope with such a busy schedule – but if Michael Jackson could tour the world then I shouldn't balk at a visit to Lowestoft.

By the fifth day of the tour I was happily into the swing of things; Grazio and Russell were happy so long as there was a snooker table in each hotel, but Fanny was showing signs of strain. Instead of her usual afternoon romp on Hampstead Heath she was staring out of the window of a Sierra Estate at meadows that would never feel the touch of her paws. The adoration of her public didn't satisfy her anymore. The long and short of it was she wanted a woof in the park. As the tour continued, Fanny's dissatisfaction with her lifestyle grew. I noticed that her appearances on stage became shorter with every show. Some nights she barely got through her impression of Barbara Windsor before waddling off into the wings. Concerned theatre managers suggested I prolong her stage performances by means of a wire hoop connected to the national grid. I hastily declined such an inhumane suggestion, but noted the mechanics of the device and used it successfully to keep Russell firmly at his piano. It's a little known fact that if Russell so much as crosses his legs, 5,000 volts shoot through his posing pouch. Sometimes I tell him to cross his legs just for the fun of it.

But if Fanny was unhappy, then so was I. It became increasingly obvious that touring around the country and performing every night was not a suitable life-style for a dog, however sophisticated that dog might be. It was not that her ego had diminished in any way, simply that she'd rather make feature films than endure the rigours of touring. And it would suit her best if such films were shot on location, preferably somewhere leafy and green with plenty of lamp-posts. Meeting Ben Elton and Jonathan Ross was all very well, but she'd rather have her nose stuck up some dog's bum in the park.* Because of her notoriety, such simple pleasures were now taboo. Every cock of her leg was covered by the paparazzi. Fame had become a prison. She remembered the days when she was just a young pup on the streets – sure, she took a few short cuts, but this was show biz and you had to get smart. And she'd stayed smart. That's why she was breaking out.

*WOULDN'T WE ALL?

And so it
was to be that
on June 4th 1988,
in front of a packed house
at the Hackney Empire, Fanny
the Wonder Dog appeared on stage
for the very last time. It was perhaps
her greatest performance. She caught the
choc-drop that night with such nonchalant
ease that the crowd rose as one. A hushed silence
fell as Fanny breathed life once more into her impressions of stage, screen and radio stars. She finished her routine
to the sound of deafening applause. It was over. She was going to be a

dog again.

There was a party that night, but I didn't feel like going. Not tonight. Fanny and I slipped quietly out of the stage door and made our way to the chip shop. As we shuffled along the wet cobblestones I fancied I saw the ghostly image of Ernie Moss leaning against an old gas light.

With a broad grin he doffed his trilby and gave me the thumbs-up sign.

And then he was gone.

Dear, patient reader – it may please you to learn that Fanny has never regretted her decision to retire from the stage. And while she has been lured back into the television studio on rare occasions, it is only to appear on programmes of the highest quality.

Trick or Treat, for example, was a televisual presentation of such brilliance that she was, on artistic grounds, unable to refuse. And while there were those at London Weekend who balked at the fee she demanded for a weekly four-second appearance, the head of Light Entertainment coughed up, it is rumoured from his own pocket.

Fanny also agrees to show herself on the occasional chat show.

However there is one ghost from the past that haunts us to this day. You will recall the feud between the Pie Faces and the Greenhalghs; a bitter dispute that has blighted many generations. Although I am proud of my Pie Face connection, I have always regarded the differences between the two clans as somewhat comical. That is until I unwittingly crossed the path of Andy Greenhalgh. He was a fire eater with a difference and I took an instant dislike to him. To be frank it wasn't a great act. He performed underwater and it mostly consisted of him sticking his head out of a water tank every few seconds and shouting *'It's gone out again!'*

Now, when several artistes are sharing a cramped dressing room, personal hygiene takes on a whole new meaning. So being on the bill with Andy Greenhalgh and his tank meant breathing through your mouth all evening. Andy never changed his water. When people complained he used to say, *'That water belonged to my grandfather! And if it's good enough for him, it's good enough for me!'*

'But it's green, it's slimy and it stinks!' I once argued.

'So was my grandfather,' he said with a wide-eyed shrug.

One night at the Comedy Store dressing room I confronted him. *'It's a health hazard!'* I shrieked.

'But it's lucky water,' he said. *'In 1924, my grandfather had his heart broken by Talullah Stanwyke, the most beautiful girl in Hackney (which isn't saying much). He never got over it. The very next day he bought this empty water-tank and threw himself into his new hobby. He lived for that water-tank. He did everything in it.'* I could almost hear the violins tuning up; while his crusty eye-lids blinked at me (it was like being winked at by a meat-pie), he continued with his pathetic monologue.

'Water wasn't easy to come by in those days. He searched long and hard.'

'I bet he did,' I muttered under my breath.

'Eventually he bought this water off a bloke in a pub in Mare Street.'

At this moment he paused for effect, and I took the opportunity to set light to his trousers. *'You're a fire eater,'* I said. *'Have some dinner.'* My laughter turned to cinders in the back of my throat as he nimbly leapt into the tank, and resurfaced a few seconds later spluttering and steaming and covered in green slime.

'Oh, it suits you,' I said, raising one eyebrow and leaving it there – for a week.

This confrontation led to a series of bitter disputes between us. The old Pie Face/Greenhalgh feud was about to explode once more. Eventually I received a terse note from my adversary:

'Meet me at dawn on Hampstead Heath. Come alone.'

Hampstead Heath measures five square miles. I camped out for eight weeks before I found the bastard. By this time we were so furious that we dispensed with the customary slap across the cheek with a leather glove – instead we wrestled across the springy turf for two days and two nights.

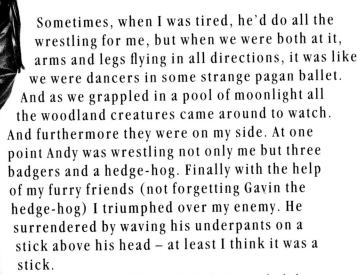

Sometimes, when I was tired, he'd do all the
wrestling for me, but when we were both at it,
arms and legs flying in all directions, it was like
we were dancers in some strange pagan ballet.
And as we grappled in a pool of moonlight all
the woodland creatures came around to watch.
And furthermore they were on my side. At one
point Andy was wrestling not only me but three
badgers and a hedge-hog. Finally with the help
of my furry friends (not forgetting Gavin the
hedge-hog) I triumphed over my enemy. He
surrendered by waving his underpants on a
stick above his head – at least I think it was a
stick.

I've had no trouble with Andy Greenhalgh
since that day. Hopefully he's learnt his lesson.
But every so often, at night, as I lie on top of my
Futon, life's cares drifting towards the ceiling, I
fancy I can hear someone dragging a water-tank
down the high street and I fear we have not yet
read the last chapter in the strange but spiteful
tale.

And so, what of the future? As Fanny and I survey the distant horizon, I cannot resist the opportunity to grant you, dear reader, a tantalising glimpse of what fate has in store . . . Hollywood is soon to be my new address. I've just signed a MAJOR DEAL with MGM, or should I say Fanny has. It seems her retirement was a sham. While I was out working, trying to earn the money to keep Fanny in the style to which she has become accustomed, she was making cow eyes at Roman Polanski. I shall tag along, perhaps as Fanny's dresser, and maybe if I smile at the right people there might be a job for me too. Who knows?

As I look back over my life with Fanny the Wonder Dog, I realise that she has manipulated events to suit her own purposes. And I suppose I wouldn't have wanted it any other way. She is a remarkable creature, a spiritual being in contact with the Universe and all the lamp-posts in it.

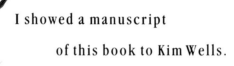

I showed a manuscript
of this book to Kim Wells.
I am still awaiting
his reply.

The Players

Gillian Pie Face . . . . Julian Clary
The Joan Collins' Fan Club . . . . Julian Clary
Mr Bishop . . . . David Clark
Miss Crogan . . . . Frankie Clary
Kim Welles . . . . Jon Hair
Santini . . . . Bob Jones
Tom Lloyd . . . . Michael Parker
Wendy Bucket . . . . Barb Jungr
Ernie Moss . . . . Paul Merton
Kingsley St Claire . . . . Ray Cooper
"Blake" . . . . Addison Cresswell
Flaxton Watercress . . . . Jules Mayhew
Nelly Clacket . . . . Emma Bernard
The lovely Russell . . . . Russell Churney
Grazio . . . . Grazio Abela

Girl with Shoe . . . . Emma Hair
Stuntman . . . . Dave "Rocky" Mountain

AND

Fanny the Wonder Dog as Herself

Mr Clary's wardrobe created by Michael Ferri

The Crew

Peter Mountain
Matthew Curtis

SHOT IN THE STUDIO OF JONATHAN LAW ASSOCIATES
AND ON LOCATION AT HACKNEY EMPIRE, THE TRAMSHED, WOOLWICH
AND NORTH END ROAD PUBLIC CONVENIENCES.

Authors' note:

'Nobody should have to live in a bed-sit'

JULIAN AND PAUL.